BASED ON A TRUE STORY

BASED ON A TRUE STORY

REAL MADE-UP MEN

MICHAEL EATON

Printed by imprintdigital
Upton Pyne, Exeter
www.digital.imprint.co.uk

Typesetting and cover design by narrator
www.narrator.me.uk
info@narrator.me.uk
033 022 300 39

Published by Shoestring Press
19 Devonshire Avenue, Beeston, Nottingham, NG9 1BS
(0115) 925 1827
www.shoestringpress.co.uk

First published 2020
© Copyright: Michael Eaton
© Cover image: Leif Gifford
© Line drawings: Linus Eaton Wattenberg

The moral right of the author has been asserted.

ISBN 978-1-912524-59-4

To Linus, in the fond hope that he will come to know more of his Poppy; and to Leif, who probably knows already.

CONTENTS

INTRODUCTION—AN ANTHROPOLOGIST WHO NEVER WAS

If you want a happy ending, that depends, of course, on where you stop your story.
– Orson Welles

Collating this bundle of hitherto unpublished pieces has provoked the question of why so much of my work has been based upon real people—the hybrid so-called 'drama-documentary'.

Among those I've dramatised: Marco Polo; Ali Akbar Mohteshemi, Iranian Minister of the Interior; Sir John 'Black Jack' Hermon, Chief Constable of the RUC; the young hussar Winston Churchill; Prime Minister John Major; Taiosoch Albert Reynolds; president George W. Bush; the gay Irish nationalist Roger Casement; Britain's most notorious serial killer Doctor Harold 'Fred' Shipman; the Victorian burglar and murderer Charlie Peace; the cultural hero of my home town Robin Hood—though there is, of course, no consensus concerning his actuality. Some of them I met. Some of them I admire. I've put words into all their mouths. There will be more in these pages.

Perhaps real people are easier to make up. Or perhaps this preoccupation to fictionalise, indeed mythologise, is a result of an ill-informed adolescent decision which led to an Initiation. My writing has been massively influenced not by literature—about which I remain largely an enthusiastic amateur—but by what Claude Lévi-Strauss termed 'The Scope of Anthropology'.

When I cockily informed my dear mother that it was my intention to apply to study Social Anthropology at university, she, not unsurprisingly, quizzed me for a definition. Disguising my ignorance, I muttered a few platitudes absorbed by osmosis from the fly-leaves of the intimidating volumes I'd recently scanned. This was, I said, a bit like Sociology (dirty word, soft subject) but about pre-industrial societies—the troubling words 'primitive', 'tribe' and 'savage' had, mercifully, already been exiled—you know, Eskimos, Australian Aborigines, Native Americans...

Lillian responded with a rousing 'Ooo-er!'—typical retort much favoured by Nottingham mams, as an expression of scepticism over the latest pretention of offspring privileged with the kind of education denied the likes of her who were forced to leave what passed for schooling to enter the slavish workforce at the unformed age of fourteen. 'You always hid behind the settee whenever the Indians came on the telly.'

This was, of course, the unvarnished truth. What more can anyone expect from a caring parent? As a child I had, indeed, been terrified at the sudden approach of Magwa, that shaven-headed Huron, the Sly Fox, Trickster nemesis of Hawkeye in the TV series distantly derived from James Fenimore Cooper's *The Last Of The Mohicans*. I have never managed to get beyond the first few pages of the ur-text, though no boy lost in the wilderness could have hoped

1

for more loyal and knowledgeable companions than those 'vanishing Americans', the eponymous Uncas and his wise father Chingachgook. He was, unsurprisingly for those days, personated not by an indigenous Mohican, but by the son of Lon Chaney, one of the greatest actors of the silent era, The Man of a Thousand Faces.

I'm still no more capable of delimiting the porous boundaries of this ultimately indefinable discipline, but what I was about to be exposed to has subsequently determined my approach to story-telling.

The Inciting Incident of my adolescent Damascene conversion took place in the Nottingham City Library, a grand Gothic Revival building from the late 1870s, a hushed temple of learning on Shakespeare Street, situated midway between school and my bus stop. This was once home to University College where D.H. Lawrence had been a far from assiduous student. I chanced—not too fated a word—to take down a slim volume, a transcription of the 1967 Reith Lectures *A Runaway World?* The question mark was no affectation, as the very first sentence posed troubling questions.

> *Men have become gods. Isn't it about time that we understood our divinity? Science offers us mastery over our environment and over our destiny, yet instead of rejoicing we feel deeply afraid. Why should this be? How might these fears be resolved?*

I was immediately hooked. The author was identified as Edmund Leach, Provost of King's College and Reader in Social Anthropology at the University of Cambridge. These were feet at which I wished to sit.

Not that I was entirely unprepared. From my paternal grandfather, Ernest Edwin Eaton, an artisan in the local trade of textile machine manufactory who was, like so many of his class and non-conformist affiliations, an autodidact member of the Mechanics Institute—which Dickens had visited on his reading tours—I had inherited bound copies of the part-work *Customs Of The World*, published by Hutchinson & Co. in 1910. Lavishly illustrated as a catalogue of exotic folk and their apparently strange but ultimately decipherable practices, the Introduction was written by A.C. Haddon M.A. Sc.D. F.R.S. This was none other than Alfred Cort Haddon, the now largely neglected pioneer who had, combatting antipathy, penury and prejudice, not only set up the teaching of Ethnology, as it was then called, at Cambridge but had been a great populariser, giving lectures to working men and women at the Horniman Museum in South London. In 1898 Haddon had led an expedition to the Torres Straits, an unintended consequence of which provided legal ammunition for the eventual granting of Native Title, still hotly contested and opposed, to indigenous Australians. Haddon was to become something of a Culture Hero.

In 2010 I would travel to the Torres Strait and make a documentary, *The Masks Of Mer,* arguing for his role as the maker of the very first ethnographic films shot 'in the field'. This was followed with *Head Hunters*, a play for BBC Radio Three, subsequently published by Shoestring Press, dramatising that expedition to the Coral Sea and how the experiences of the young members of Haddon's team later influenced the understanding and treatment of neuroses in the Great War—'shell-shock.'

Seeds planted in childhood grow to bear unlikely fruit. For the structuralist, I would learn, a weed is but a flower 'out of place.'

For reasons too tedious and too painful to recall I never made the grade as 'a proper anthropologist'. My attempt to 'do field work' in Papua New Guinea was bureaucratically stymied. I may not have been equipped with the physical stamina, the psychological stability or the intellectual shrewdness to undergo the necessary Rites of Passage. Instead I somehow found myself working on 41st Street in Manhattan (one block from stardom) as the lowest face on the totem pole of Market Research—a commercially distorted form of sociological enquiry. There I assisted in the marketing of a 'Healthy Cigarette', the plastic appendage of which possibly contained more toxic chemicals than the tobacco smoke it was 'scientifically' manufactured to filter. This seemed like the culmination of a destiny. During the war my mother had worked for the local company, John Player and Sons. She was churning out Navy Cut, with its logo of the resolute bearded sailor of HMS Hero flanked by Nottingham Castle, while my dad was lighting them up on a Destroyer in the Arctic convoys. I had a summer vacation job in the Players Bonded Warehouse and on my last day the foreman sidled up: 'Why do you want to go back to university? You could have a job for life here.' He had a point—exceptional canteen food and all the fags you could smoke. But return I did. The cigarette warehouse now stands as a glorious brutalist ruin.

When I told the school's Head of English that I was going to apply to King's he smirked: 'They're all drug addicts and homosexuals there… So you'll fit in.' He might have added 'communist spies' to scoop the trifecta. Mister Chairman, I am not now nor ever have I been… But some of my best friends…

Equipped with the Cloak of Ignorance—characteristic garb of the bullet-proof teenage know-all—I hitch-hiked down (for some reason 'they' say 'up') to that misty fen-land establishment to face the Admissions Tutor. Fortunately, this Threshold Guardian was more than benign. He was, and is, a Physical Anthropologist whose academic speciality has been the brain power of early hominids. I am forever grateful to him for indulging my own lack of cranial capacity during that interview. He had made it a mission to open the gates of this privileged establishment to wider social classes than heretofore, to champion a more ethnically diverse intake, and to attract an equal number of (gasp!) female students. King's was, in the early 1970s, one of only three co-ed colleges.

The necessary riddles were posed. What anthropological books I had read? I was able, in all truthfulness, to respond: *A World On The Wane*, a translation of *Tristes Tropiques*, the only work of Lévi-Strauss on those library shelves. I did not admit, however, that I'd stumbled through this, his most accessible work, with scant knowledge of that towering intellectual's central position in French intellectual life and thought. Nor did I know that I'd spend the best part of the next four years stretching my synapses to get to grips with his more challenging

3

oeuvre. Having attempted to re-read some of this work in recent years I am forced to ask myself the disturbing questions: Was I was deluding myself then? Or have I become much more stupid now?

I might well have fallen at the first hurdle, though, when I proudly admitted to having ploughed through *The Golden Bough*—albeit in the abridged version which was still getting on for a thousand pages. How could an eighteen-year-old about to take his A-level in Religious Knowledge have understood the scholarly detestation, the fundamental antipathy, that Provost Leach, now Sir Edmund, whom I devoutly wished to be my Mentor, held for Sir James George Frazer?

Frazer was everything Leach despised. J.G. was a social Darwinist 'armchair anthropologist' who never set foot outside of his library in Trinity College to observe how real living people, of whom it seems he was terrified, actually practised those customs, the cataloguing of which secured his fame and fortune. For Edmund Leach the author of *The Golden Bough* was an embarrassment to anthropology and Frazer was little more than a dilettante whose popularist success had cast a blighted shadow over a Cinderella social science, the ultimate purpose of which should be to demonstrate how the apparently exotic beliefs and bizarre practices of peoples who seemed so distant from 'us', were not, all things considered, so very different from our own mental processes.

Anyway, I passed the audition and progressed into the Liminal Zone.

Leach's caveats notwithstanding, I continue to hold Frazer in some regard. In his depiction of the similarities of the central character of the Christian story to other resurrected deities, Attis, Adonis and Osiris among them, Frazer, perhaps inadvertently, provoked many lay readers to doubt the faith of their fathers.

As a graduate student, one summer afternoon when I was pretending to work in the Haddon Library—named after that chap whose work I had unknowingly absorbed in my grand-dad's *Customs Of The World*—the librarian asked if I'd be interested in earning a few quid: a consignment had to be carted to the library from Trinity College. This was an offer impossible to resist, and I corralled a chum to share in this unexpected bounty. Equipped with a wonky trolley, we set off for Isaac Newton's *alma mater*. Dozens of cardboard boxes were piled up in the Trinity Porter's Lodge—we'd surely be earning our crust. Only an existentialist could have come up with the catchphrase *Il faut imaginer Sisyphe heureux*. On the third sweaty trip we stopped for what Australians call a 'smoko', *de rigeur* in those dear dead days beyond recall. I used to puff on exotic Camels (one hump or two?) whilst my comrade favoured Old Holborn roll-ups from the metropolis of his birth. I had a sudden desire to unearth exactly what we were hauling. So we opened a box to discover... this was nothing less than the contents of Sir James George Frazer's library!

These were volumes of traveller's tales, missionary memoirs, colonial accounts, with titles such as 'Across The Hindu Kush On A Tandem', 'The Gospel Light Among The Cannibals', 'Reports Of The District Commissioner for Matabeleland.'. Flipping through these yellowing pages we were transported

4

into the mind of the 'Father of Anthropology' (*pace* Sir Edmund) who had meticulously underlined any sentence which would bolster his fundamental thesis that all human endeavour—evolving from Superstition before arriving at modern Scientific Rationality—was ultimately performed to ensure the proliferation of the harvest—what one contemptuous contemporary critic called: 'The Covent Garden Theory of Religion.'

This is, of course, to belittle the diligence of Frazer's work—the Old Man has suffered enough. For me, it was a magical moment which left a profound impression.

Many years later I went to a book sale at Nottingham Central Library—now relocated from that erstwhile inspiring building to an ugly erection on the inaptly named Angel Row—where I picked up for a pound apiece all twelve volumes of the Third Edition of Frazer's masterwork, massively expanded from the cut-down version I'd slogged through before my university interview. I have become particularly fond of the final volume which contains the Bibliography and Index—fruit of his assiduous labours in all those books we'd been carting.

Frazer the rationalist would doubtless be spinning in his sepulchre at my dissident practice of opening any page at random to reveal an inventory of unintended surrealist poetry, always resonating with the overwhelming strangeness of humanity's organisation of social life in a never-ending struggle to make sense of the business of being.

Consider, for example, two elementary binary oppositions:

BLACK

- *animals in rain charms, as scapegoats;*
- *bull sacrificed to the dead;*
- *cats, witches turn into;*
- *drink, an emetic;*
- *goat-skin, in relation to Dionysus;*
- *god among the Slavs;*
- *hair, homeopathic charm to restore;*
- *Mountains, in France, sleeping witch in the;*
- *ox in magic, bath of blood of;*
- *poplars, mistletoe on;*
- *snake clan of the Warramunga;*
- *spauld, a disease of cattle, cure for;*
- *three-legged horse ridden by witches;*
- *victims in rain making;*
- *and white in relation to human scapegoats.*

- *faces and bodies of man-slayers painted;*
- *widows painted;*
- *lion-killer painted;*
- *as a colour to repel demons;*
- *figs worn by human scapegoats.*
- *birds, souls of dead kings incarnate in;*
- *bull, soul of a dead king incarnate in a;*
- *bulls sacrificed to Jupiter;*
- *bulls, sacrificed by Druids at cutting the mistletoe;*
- *chalk, bodies of newly initiated lads coated with;*
- *clay, Caffre boys at circumcision smeared with;*
- *bodies of novices at initiation smeared with;*
- *cloth, mistletoe caught in a;*
- *cloth, used to catch the Midsummer bloom of the oak;*
- *cock buried at a boundary;*
- *cock burnt in Midsummer bonfire;*
- *crosses made by the King of the Bean;*
- *disease transferred to a scapegoat;*
- *dog, Iroquois sacrifice of a;*
- *herb, external souls of two brothers in a;*
- *horse, effigy of, carried through Midsummer fire;*
- *mice spared by Bohemian peasants;*
- *ox, sacrament of, among the Abchases:*
- *ram, consecration of a, among the Kalmucks;*
- *and red wool in ceremony of the expulsion of evils;*
- *roses dyed red by the blood of Aphrodite;*
- *sails that turned black;*
- *snake eaten to acquire supernatural knowledge;*
- *thorn, a charm against witches;*
- *victims sacrificed for sunshine;*
- *sacred among the Aryans.*

If this is not Science it surely is Art.

*

'Culture' for the anthropologist, I would come to learn, has a much wider 'scope' than any delineation by the Arts Council or by aficionados of BBC Radio Three—more egalitarian and inclusive than Matthew Arnold's famous definition *'the pursuit of our total perfection by means of getting to know, on all the matters which most concern us, the best which has been thought and said in the world.'* Rather than a product of selective education, Culture is what we, as a species, do, how we communicate symbolically in an ever-shifting dialectic with Nature—itself, of course, a constantly transforming category circumscribed by human language. Such a definition demands interpretation of the underlying codes of how we attempt to make sense of the world. Our customs are every bit as exotic as those catalogued in *The Golden Bough*.

Another litany, this one from 1937:

- *Behaviour of people at war memorials;*
- *Shouts and gestures of motorists;*
- *The aspidistra cult;*
- *Football pools;*
- *Bathroom behaviour;*
- *Beards, armpits, eyebrows;*
- *Anti-semitism;*
- *Distribution, diffusion and significance of the dirty joke;*
- *Funerals and undertakers;*
- *Female taboos about eating;*
- *The private life of midwives.*

This manifesto was the work of Tom Harrison who, having been taught by Haddon, had recently returned from fieldwork in the South Sea islands of the New Hebrides (Vanuatu since independence). Unveiled in the *New Statesman* to announce the inauguration of Mass Observation, 'An Anthropology of Our People', it was co-signed by the poet, journalist and Communist Party member Charles Madge and Humphrey Jennings—whom Lindsay Anderson dubbed 'the only true poet that British cinema has yet produced' because of the wonderful documentary films he later made during the Second World War. At this point Jennings was known, if at all, as a would-be artist and one of the organisers of the notorious surrealist exhibition at the New Burlington Galleries. The Guest of Honour, Salvador Dali, made a characteristically flamboyant appearance in a deep-sea diver's suit, from which he had to be forcibly extracted before lack of oxygen could have resulted in a fatally unintended consequence.

Such an approach to Culture ought to preclude reaching for a revolver.

*

Perhaps the most important insight from anthropological thought for the storyteller, however, derives from the analysis of ritual—the way our species transforms the natural movement from birth to death into the cultural journey through life.

Ritual does not, as in popular parlance, imply meaningless routine. Ritual is a dynamic process without which the biological passage through existence would have no social value. The founding interpretation of 'rituals of transition' is *Les Rites de*

Passage by Arnold van Gennep, published in 1909. In this inspirational work the Dutch folklorist examined ceremonies which mark an individual's movement through the 'crises of life': the transition, say, from boyhood to manhood; from maidenhood to motherhood; from single to married; from worker to soldier; from living being to dead ancestor—whatever seems natural is in fact an expression of the cultural. Van Gennep drew on examples from all historical periods and geographical regions to establish that underlying these social processes is a deep-structural 'schema' which is invariably, but never predictably, organized into three parts.

Even in our own ritually impoverished existence such critical transformations must be marked through ceremonies, however perfunctory. Without the proper mumbled words and the public presentation of the correct piece of paper any confidence trickster or bigamist could pretend to be a doctor, a bishop, a High Court judge, a bachelor. How else would anyone know how to treat them?

However, a successful journey from one socially sanctioned position to another—from status A to status B—is always a tricky business, never easily accomplished. Each of these conditions carries with it appropriate behaviours, necessary obligations, comfortable securities. A gap is rent in the social fabric when a person departs from the initial condition. And room to incorporate the new member must be allowed in the role to be fulfilled.

It follows, therefore, that there has to be a transitional period in this processional movement when status A has been left but before status B has been attained—a time when the 'normal' rules of neither role apply. Van Gennep called this troubling betwixt-and-between state *les marges*, the margins. For his great British disciple Victor Turner, who moved seamlessly from anthropology to the ritual space of theatre, this was 'liminality'.

During this neither/nor period, initiates must be separated, not only physically but psychically, from their existing state—to which they might, at first, be unwilling to leave and desperate to return—and taught, often through violence and mental disturbance, the rules which will govern the future role the social world demands of them. Liminality is a perilous ordeal.

For instance, when Alfred Haddon led his 1898 ethnographic expedition to Mer in the Torres Strait he was told by the male elders of the island who had come to trust him, of the initiation ceremonies they had undergone by which Boys became Men. These rituals had been suppressed since the arrival of Christian missionaries and were now spoken of only in conditions of great secrecy. At a time when the first hairs began to appear on the faces of adolescent lads they were separated from their mothers and taken by the older initiated men to a *kwod*, a sanctified space neither village nor garden, where for a period of several gruelling months the lore, sacred and profane, they would need to know would be imparted to them before they could return to the world as grown-up men. Forced to abandon their usual clothing, they would be taught expertise in fishing magic, property rights, sexual mores, the arts of warfare, the practices of headhunting, the movement of the tides, navigation by the stars and, most arcane of all, the time-honoured hidden spiritual beliefs which could never be revealed to the uninitiated—to women, to children, to strangers—upon pain of death. The female inhabitants of Mer also, of course, held their own wisdom, which, for male anthropologists, would remain veiled in a cloud of mystery.

Liminal life in this all-male 'boot-camp' must have been a tough business, otherwise the lessons burned into the minds and bodies of the initiates would have scant significance and they would not feel justified in imposing these hard-won lessons upon the youngsters who would come to follow them in their turn. When this process was over, their return to the life of everyday social relations would be marked by ceremonies and dances to certify their re-arrival. Later in life there would be further ritual ordeals to face.

This tripartite schema—the separation from the initial status, the leap into the unknown, the eventual incorporation into a new normal—cannot but be reminiscent of the shape of the tale. From Aristotle's well-known maxim in the *Poetics*: 'Every story must have a Beginning, a Middle and an End' (though, as Jean-Luc Godard famously quipped: 'But not necessarily in that order'), to the grizzled movie producer's formula: 'Get your hero up a tree, throw rocks at him, get him out of the tree' (though I can't help but wonder: 'What if our hero enjoys being pelted by rocks?') the pattern of narrative mirrors the structure of ritual from which, it seems to me, it ultimately derives.

Classical tragedy results in destruction or death—but the journey of Tragic Heroes would be meaningless if they had not gained some painful insight into what fatal flaw had led them to the inevitable—otherwise the Protagonist would be an idiot signifying nothing and provoking neither our Fear nor our Pity. Best to exempt the intervention of the *deus ex machina*, the supernatural entity appearing, literally, from the skies to tie up the loose ends and resolve the conflicts mortals have been unable to sort out for themselves—this takes us back to Lévi-Strauss, for whom Myth is an attempt to resolve contradictions between Nature and Culture which can never have a fixed and final solution.

Classical comedy so often ends in Marriage—but the young lovers must engage in liminal combat with the obstacles set up by old forces contriving to prevent their union and they must learn that this agèd authority can be conquered.

Ritual reveals that all stories are predicated upon the protagonist's lack—some object or quality they don't have but they need to move forward, whether they realise this or not. When Dorothy comes back to the monochromatic Kansas farm after her technicolor quest over the rainbow she provides a moment of closure: *'There's no place like home'*. But having donned those ruby slippers—metonym of the rite of passage from powerless Girl to Young Woman with agency—this will no longer be the same psychic place from which the whirlwind swept her. On her journey down the Yellow Brick Road she has gained knowledge: she has learned the value of friendship; she has learnt that those in control are paper tigers ('Pay no attention to that man behind the curtain') who need not be feared; she has learnt that the power she needs to equip her through the next stage of life's journey lies within her.

Social life is a never-ending journey—not only a continuing movement from one status to the next, but a gnostic quest leading from a lack of knowledge to a greater comprehension. At least, that is surely our fond hope.

The Liminal Zone is the space of Story. And I've been stuck there ever since I took down that slim volume in Nottingham library. Each time 'The End' is written—the only two words writers enjoy—another beginning beckons.

All the world's an ashtray and all the men and women merely Players.

'HOME FROM HOME'—GRAHAM GREENE IN NOTTINGHAM

'...the focal point of failure, a place undisturbed by ambition, a place to be resigned to...'

On the face of it, not a very flattering trio of epithets about our town.

This judgment was written nearly fifty years after these impressions of Nottingham were first experienced. The writer had only considered a resort into autobiography on the advice of a psychiatrist. He was suffering from acute depressions and, as he tells it, had demanded shock treatment. The analyst counselled him to stick with his pain and to write down memories of his younger self. The writer in his late 60s was only thinking about the Nottingham of his early 20s as part of a process of therapy.

Young Graham Greene

Graham Greene was not as other adolescents. His particular version of self-abuse involved pushing a six-chambered revolver loaded with one live bullet into his ear and pulling the trigger—Berkhamsted Roulette. Fortunately for all of us his attempt to escape this life was thwarted and he gave up betting on his own death when the process ceased to thrill him. Instead he settled upon a more lasting, if no less anti-social, method of numbing the pain of existence—he became a writer.

Writing is a form of therapy; sometimes I wonder how all those who do not write, compose or paint can manage to escape the madness, the melancholia, the panic fear which is inherent in the human condition.

Having determined upon this course of action he had to seek, as all unpublished writers must, some form of subsidy for his new-found solitary vice. It was in pursuit of such a career that, on a freezing wet night in the winter of 1925, his train pulled into Nottingham, the furthest north this 21-year old who was born in the Home Counties and had studied at Oxford had yet travelled.

Remembering this arrival, he wrote in his 1971 autobiography *A Sort of Life*:

I arrived one wet night in Nottingham and woke next morning in the unknown city to an equally dark day. This was not like a London smog; the streets were free of vapour, the electric lights shone clearly; the fog lay out of sight far above the lamps. When I read Dickens on Victorian London I think of Nottingham in the twenties. There was an elderly 'boots' still employed in the Black Dog Inn, there were girls suffering from unemployment in the lace trade, who would, so it is said, sleep with you in return for a high tea with muffins, and a haggard blue-haired prostitute, ruined by amateur competition, haunted the corner by W.H. Smith's bookshop. Trams rattled downhill through the goose-market and onto the blackened castle. Against the rockface leant the oldest pub in England with all the grades of a social guide: the private bar, the saloon, the ladies', the snug, the public. Little dark cinemas offered matinee seats for fourpence in the stalls.

Little did he know it, but Graham Greene had discovered that strange, seedy country of the mind: Greene had arrived in Greene-land. It was a term he grew to hate but he had to admit that *'it is the land in which I have passed much of my life.'* As he fictionalised the castle in *A Gun for Sale* (1936, of which more later):

It wasn't really a castle any longer. It was a yellow brick municipal museum full of flint arrowheads and pieces of broken brown pottery and a few stags' heads in the zoological section suffering from moths and one mummy brought back from Egypt by the Earl of Nottwich in 1843.

The Market Place

The prolific, and now unread, Nottingham author Cecil Roberts responded in his spluttering review:

There is not and never has been such a thing [as the 'goose market']. He has muddled this with the annual Goose Fair a four day kermasse of round-a-bouts, helter-skelters, fat women and animal shows once held in the Market Place. From the time of the Norman Conquest...it was known and is known as The Market Place, the largest in the kingdom. He talks of the Black Dog Hotel. There is no such hotel. He means the Black Boy.

The Black Boy Hotel (above); Nottingham Castle (below)

True enough. But if you're going to nit-pick, Mister R., the Black Dog conveys a much more Greenian ethos.

*

Greene came to Nottingham to learn the craft of newspaper sub-editing. No national newspaper would take on someone without experience and there was no apprentice scheme. So, by pestering Sir Charles Starmer, the owner of a chain of provincial papers, he managed to secure an unpaid appointment in the editorial offices of the *Nottingham Journal*, which he described at first as '*a third rate paper, run by third class people*'. This was an opinion he was later to revise, perhaps it is no condemnation as he had a life-long sympathy with the flawed and the imperfect.

The paper was housed in the splendidly over-wrought Watson Fothergill building on Parliament Street which had been built for the Nottingham *Daily Express* in 1876. It was originally a two-storey edifice with a Gothic tower, reminiscent of the work of one of Fothergill's architectural mentors, William Burges. But a third storey, still present today, was added in 1899. The *Express* was a paper of Liberal sympathies and the heads of Cobden, Bright and Gladstone (although some say it is Palmerstone!) are carved into the entrance hall. Greene described it as:

(A) narrow stone Gothic door, stained with soot, which resembled the portal of a Pugin chapel, and the heads of Liberal statesmen stuck out above like gargoyles: on rainy days the nose of Gladstone dripped on my head as I came in.

Journal Heads

Although the paper was 'vulgar', it could boast that J.M. Barrie had once been a member of its staff. This was impressive to the would-be novelist who confesses that his 'unfashionable taste' was predisposed towards Barrie. '*Childhood is not afraid of sentimentality.*'

Coincidentally *Peter Pan* was playing at the Theatre Royal while he was in town. I wonder if he went to see it? Not many people know that Peter Pan was a Nottingham lad. During his short spell in our city Barrie went for a stroll one Sunday with a lady friend at the local beauty spot, Clifton Grove—alas long since over-taken by progress. He saw a boy with his pocket handkerchief fastened by a safety pin to the back pocket of his short trousers and Barrie remarked that he had lost his shadow and his mother has pinned it back on. Of such trivial incidents are enduring legends born.

Greene worked from 5.30 p.m. till midnight, learning to sub the reports coming in on telegrams from all over the country, tackling the intricacies of headline settings and determining the value of the local news items. Though 'happiness' is not a word frequently associated with either the life or the works of Graham Greene, he seems, on occasion at least, to have been genuinely happy among these cheerful, friendly subs with their strong Notts. accents.

We sit around a table together, with the News Editor… at the head and snip and blue pencil and talk and smoke away, like a family party. And just before ten someone goes out and buys two penny parcels of hot potato chips to eat and the bald old Irishman who does the Sporting page puts on the kettle and makes tea… And there's a huge fat man with rather long hair who does the Angling notes who wanders in about 10.30 and keeps everybody from working by telling endless tall fish stories.

If we look at the news stories of that bleak winter of November 1925– February 1926 we see that they, like Greene's letters and memories, are dominated by the weather. It was a terrible winter with heavy snowfalls and disasters by road, rail and sea.

At Griffin and Spalding's Winter Sale Ladies Hats were down from 63 shillings and corsets reduced from 8/11d to a mere five bob. County were at the bottom of the First Division and Forest struggling fourth from the bottom of the Second. Though Labour had won three seats off the Tories in the November council elections, on the national level the seeds of the General Strike were being sown when the coal-owners refused the miners' demands for a wage rise and their trade union leaders called for nationalisation of the pits with compensation for the owners. There was trouble in Russia… trouble in Iraq… trouble in China.

Of the local stories printed in the penny journal one of the most intriguing was a court report of a Catholic priest who was on trial for graffiti-ing (if such a word then existed) the walls of the house of the landlord of the *Hearty Good Fellow* (which used to be on Maid Marion Way). Among the messages were:

'Hope the gas goes out.'
'The curse of God, Amen' and
'How's your skin for a rabbit?'

The paper gives no motivation for this bizarre behaviour but there were calls for the cryptic priest to be de-frocked. He sounds to me, although there is absolutely no evidence for this, like a Greene character in embryo, someone we will meet later in the pages of *A Gun For Sale*.

*

For most of the time Greene spent in Nottingham he lived, with his dog Paddy, *'a rough-haired terrier with orange and brown bits,'* in *'cheap lodgings…in a grim grey row with a grim grey name, Ivy House All Saints Terrace',* presided over by a *'thin complaining widow',* one Missis Loney (another improbably appropriate name). Full board was apparently thirty-five shillings a week including use of a sitting room which was *'quite large and has bird wallpaper, the door has carved panels, leaves in the bottom ones and large figures…of Diana and Ceres.'* Very tasteful.

Every morning, before struggling with his first *'hopeless'* novel, he would take his dog for a walk in the nearby Arboretum, under the *'barely visible'* skies, where *'when you touched the leaves they left soot on the fingers'*. The park, in *A Gun for Sale* becomes *'a place of dull wilted trees and palings and gravel paths for perambulators'*.

Really, the town, *'misty and with pavements deep in slush',* might almost have been custom-made for him!

Greene was once to state that, as a novelist: *'I cannot invent'* and his intrepid biographer, Norman Sherry, (in *The Life of Graham Greene, Volume One 1904-1939,* first published in 1989) catalogued the ways in which his lodgings were recycled: *'whenever he needed to describe a disreputable house he returned to Ivy House.'*

It perhaps comes as no surprise that the exact location of these lodgings is somewhat in dispute. For what is All Saints Terrace these days is perhaps not what it was when young Greene was a resident. Such ambiguity is meat and potatoes for local psycho-geographers.

He always considered the house to be haunted with an *'evil influence'* that meant he never got an uninterrupted night's sleep—perhaps it was those chips. The lodging was pressed into service in *Brighton Rock* (1938) and four years earlier in *It's a Battlefield*, which also transforms his landlady into a Missis Coney, a *'meek, suspicious woman.'* Ivy House was finally put to rest in a rather strange metaphysical play *The Potting Shed*, written in 1957. Greene confessed that he had trouble getting this to work:

> *I was on another visit to Malaya (in 1956) and I only discovered the flaw after I'd smoked a pipe or two of opium. Thanks to the peace and quiet these afforded me I was able to mend the play.*

I have never seen it performed, but having read it, one can only speculate what it must have been like before the influence of the poppy.

Suffice it to say here that the central character, James Callifer, to whom something supernatural has happened in the potting shed, is a sub-editor on the *Journal* in furnished lodgings in Nottingham. The stage directions read: *'the furniture is his landlady's and could belong to nobody but a landlady: the bobbed fringes of the sage-green tablecloth, the sideboard with a mirror, the glass biscuit-box with a silver top, the Marcus Stone engravings.'*

Old memories die hard.

*

A SHORT DIGRESSION ON THE ARBORETUM.

In 1850 the Inclosure Act Commissions acquired twelve acres of land which were destined to become a city centre park. At its opening in 1852 a local poet, Edward Hind, penned the following celebratory verse, worthy of the Great McGonigle himself (note once again the meteorological leitmotif):

> *And everyone eagerly joins in the fun*
> *Some playing at kissing,*
> *Some dancing, some courting,*
> *Some smoking, some joking,*
> *Some laughing, some sporting.*
> *And despite of the dust and the threatening weather*
> *Ten thousand souls all feel happy together.*

The Arboretum

*

Most afternoons Greene escaped by going to the pictures. It has become a cliché to state that, of all great modern novelists, Greene's work is most influenced by the cinema. Over thirty of his works have been filmed and he

17

wrote many original screenplays as well as being an influential film critic in the 1930s. His originality as a critic perhaps lay in the fact that he was in no way sniffy about the staple fare of entertainment cinema—he admits to preferring Westerns, thrillers and comedies to the more pretentious aspirations of the so-called seventh art.

Similarly, his originality (and readability) as a writer derives from the fact that his tales, though grounded in a complex morality, are never scared to embrace the pace and excitement of conventions more usually associated with popular fiction.

Though Greene, for a while, separated what he called his 'entertainments' from what presumably he considered his more serious fiction it is hard for this reader, at least, to make that distinction fit.

But whatever the effect of cinematic narrative on his own work, his passion for the movies, his love, indeed, of going to the cinema is in no doubt. While he was living in Nottingham he could have seen such classic first runs as: Tom Mix in an adaptation of Zane Grey's *The Riders of the Purple Sage* (which is great); Chaplin's *The Gold Rush* (which is even greater); Keaton's *Seven Chances* (which is a masterpiece); Lon Chaney in *The Unholy Three* (yet another timeless work from the Man with a Thousand Faces); the first version of *The Wizard of Oz* starring that unfortunately named silent comedian Larry Semon (which, unfortunately, is anything but great); and Pola Negri in *East of Suez* (which can't be seen because it's lost but was probably really terrific because it was directed by Raoul Walsh from a play by Somerset Maugham). But he mentions none of these. Instead he records seeing *Smouldering Fires* directed by Clarence Brown and starring Pauline Frederick (which is a wonderfully ground-breaking melodrama concerning a middle-aged businesswoman who falls for a young man working in her factory and… stop me, I could go on); and *Satan's Sister* (not known to exist but dearly sought by the many aficionados of the adorable Betty Balfour, England's favourite home-grown star, and helmed by the ever-dependable George Pearson.)

Oh, what thrill it must have been to be a spectator of the Silver Screen in that Golden Age!

However, the puritanical and, indeed, misogynistic side of the sensitive young man and future film critic seems to have been uppermost in causing his particular aversion to the Latin lover, Rudolph Valentino, whom he characterised in a letter of the time as a: *'gross fleshy animal… But all the shop girls and stout matrons…go and are thrilled.'*

One movie he did like, though, describing it as *'much the most successful effort I've seen'* was *The Black Pirate* with Douglas Fairbanks—I wonder whether the cinema he attended was equipped to show the recently-restored two colour Technicolor version?

In Greene's second book of memoirs, *Ways of Escape* (1980), he reminisces with affection about *'all those Empires and Odeons of a luxury and an extravagance which we will never see again.'* Though he never names any of the screens he visited in Nottingham, and there were dozens in the city at that time, it is a pretty safe bet that he must have gone to the cinema which was closest to his place of work and which was, at that time, one of the grandest in the land. I'm sure it was this picture palace he describes as 'great' and 'gaudy' in *A Gun for Sale*.

*

A LONGER DIGRESSION ON THE ELITE.

The Elite was opened on August 22nd 1921, at a time when Britain could boast of twenty million cinema admissions per week and (though by what mode of economic analysis this statistic was arrived at I am unsure) the cinema was said to be the fifth largest industry in the world. Given this industrial buoyancy perhaps the statues of Art, Drama, Music, Literature and Justice which adorn the facade of the 1,500-seater Parliament Street cinema seem understandable if none the less pretentious.

Inside there were cafes, dining rooms, banqueting halls and ballrooms of every inappropriate architectural style—the Georgian, the Dutch, the Louis Seize, even a modern American soda fountain and, in pride of place, the largest cinema organ in these isles with seventy-seven stops and no fewer than three thousand pipes, augmenting, of course, the orchestra.

The Elite: the exterior (top left); the auditorium (top right);
the lobby (bottom left); the dining room (bottom centre); the Tudor tea rooms (bottom right)

The guide-book which commemorated the Elite's opening (a copy of which can be consulted in the Nottingham Local History Library) does not, quite rightly, hold back in trumpeting the luxury available to any citizen who could afford the price of admission:

A picture theatre befitting the high status of the city—a perfect princely refuge in which, under the magic spell of the screen one may lose sight of the dull and frequently sordid facts of everyday existence. Here has been created an atmosphere conducive to the dreaming of dreams and affording a soothing and refreshing sense of isolation from the outside world. In these strenuous days the value of such a refuge can hardly be set too high: to be able to sustain oneself with the thought that at the end of the weary day one may of a certainty find a delightful door of escape into that boundless life of the screen… Once inside our Picture Theatre… we shed our mundane entities and become gods, free of the whole wide world, free to enter intimately into the lives of interesting folk in every clime and of all degrees… the once-coveted seven league boots would be a positive hindrance now we move the portal to Dreamland. True Magic indeed!

Greene describes the prime motivation of his life as *'escape'*. And the cinema remained for him *'an escape for an hour and a half from the melancholy which falls inexorably round the novelist when he has lived for too many months on end in his private world.'*

Well, he could have found no more conducive location than the Elite Picture Theatre.

Perhaps the nadir of this once great palace of entertainment was attained in the middle 1970s, shortly before the Elite became a bingo-hall. It was then owned by the ABC chain and was still a single-screener. Lest anyone might think the following sounds like what folklorists call a 'FOAF tale', heard from a Friend Of A Friend, let me assure you it was conveyed first-hand from a chum who was then the Assistant Manager.

That summer the latest cinematic novelty was Sensuround which accompanied an otherwise unexciting disaster movie called *Earthquake*. With a combination of an eerie high-pitched whine that only dogs might hear and some state-of-the-art electronically-devised shuddering of the seats patrons would succumb to the thrilling illusion that tall buildings were falling on them. The cost of hiring and installing this equipment meant that the management could only see a profit if the picture enjoyed a lengthy run, so *Earthquake* was booked to play exclusively for six weeks. Doubts as to the sagacity of this investment were raised when at the first afternoon show, which played to half a dozen desultory spectators in that age before mass unemployment, the Sensuround set off the alarm system in the jeweller's next door. But the real disaster took place that evening in the auditorium rather than on the screen. The famous Louis Seize ballroom above the cinema had been long abandoned by human patrons but had become the domicile of an army of mice which fed upon the once-grand plaster-work. Evidently startled by this latest desperate gimmick they fled the ballroom and scurried in one rodentine wave into the stalls. The Elite became a Hamelin without a Pied Piper as terrified customers screamed, but not at the strained plight of Charlton Heston as he battled with the San Andreas fault.

True Magic indeed!

But it was not in the cinema, but in another imposing edifice that Greene was to find his salvation. For it was while he was in Nottingham that an event occurred which was to define the moral journey of the rest of his life.

*

The letters Greene wrote recording his impressions of the city, cited by Sherry, were addressed to Miss Vivien Dayrell-Browning, his recent fiancée. They met under rather strange circumstances at university. What brought them together was a film review!

Greene had written an article in a student paper which revealed the adolescent male virgin's fascination with and fear and loathing of sex:

> *We either go to Church and worship the Virgin Mary or to a public house and snigger over stories and limericks; and this exaggeration of the sex instinct has had a bad effect on art, on the cinematograph as well as on the stage.*

A very cross letter arrived pointing out that Catholics did not 'worship' the Madonna, the correct theological term was apparently 'hyperdulia'. Greene wrote an apologetic reply inviting his critic to tea. Vivien arrived and it was love at first slight.

Greene wrote his mother that: *'she's turned out very charming and not nearly so religious as her furious letter made me believe. So once again out of the lion has come forth sweetness!'* (Echoes of a Tate and Lyle treacle tin more than the original quotation from the Book of Judges?)

However, she was a devout Catholic. Marriage was inconceivable unless Greene would, as he put it, *'embrace the Scarlet Woman.'* Perhaps it was out of embarrassment that he chose the idiom of doggerel to let Vivien know he was sniffing round her faith:

> *Put out your right foot,*
> *Pray the shoe's tight:*
> *The C. of E.'s crumbling,*
> *Rome may be right.*

Her reply to this sounds like something from Noel Coward: *'Oh, Graham!! How perfectly marvellous… Madly excited.'*

YET ANOTHER DIGRESSION ON SAINT BARNABAS CATHEDRAL.

Pugin designed Nottingham's Roman Catholic cathedral in his sternest, most uncompromisingly Gothic revivalist mode. It was a real shame the building was scrubbed down some years ago and revealed its rather soft honey-coloured

Derbyshire stone—it was originally designed to have been constructed in red brick. The cathedral's sooty exterior seemed to suit its cramped Derby Road location adding to, in Greene's words, its *'inconceivable and incredible... power'.*

Saint Barnabas was being built, not without terrible anti-Catholic sectarian opposition, at the same time as, in 1843, the RC convert, Augustus Welby Pugin, was writing his celebrated argument for the use of the Gothic: *An Apology for the Revival of Christian Architecture.* Though he is credited as being one of the most influential proponents of the Gothic revival it is worth remembering that Pugin championed the Gothic primarily in relation to ecclesiastical architecture, for it spoke of an idiom which pre-dated his least favourite epoch, the Reformation. He considered this one of his best buildings declaring that it had *'a grand appearance, though perfectly plain and admit(ting) of the most solemn and rich interior.'*

Saint Barnabas Cathedral

*

Greene says that he was led there only out of a desire to *'learn the nature and limits of the beliefs (Vivien) held. It was only fair, since she knew what I believed—in nothing supernatural.'*

Yet, despite his protestations, in a few short weeks he had come to accept the Holy Roman Church, intellectually if perhaps not yet emotionally, and he continued a believer for the rest of his life, though some would describe him as a rather heretical one, and he would describe himself as a Protestant within the Church of Rome.

How fortunate he was (if that is how these matters are to be assessed) to have his call for instruction answered by the Administrator of the Cathedral, Father Trollope, another character, with a possibly inappropriate name, who could have been a product of Greene's own imagination.

(A)t the first sight he was all I detested most in my private image of the Church. A very tall and very fat man with big smooth jowls which looked as though they had never needed a razor, he resembled closely a character in one of those nineteenth-century paintings to be seen in art shops on the wrong side of Piccadilly— monks and cardinals enjoying their Friday abstinence by dismembering enormous lobsters and pouring great goblets of wine. Poor Trollope, his appearance maligned him. He led a very ascetic life, and one of the worst privations was a rule which, at that period, forbade him to visit the theatre, for he had been an actor in the West End... There were many plays on his shelves among the theological books—reading them was the nearest he could get to the footlights.

Father Trollope

This is how Greene remembered Trollope in *A Sort of Life*, but there is an earlier record in his first travel book, published in 1936, *Journey Without Maps*, in which, incidentally, there was another meteorologically monochromatic memory of Nottingham:

> *The fog came down in the morning and stayed till night. It wasn't a disagreeable fog; it lay heavy and black between the sun and the earth; there was no light, but the air was clear.*

About poor Father Trollope Greene remembers how his instructions in the faith were often conducted on the top decks of trams so that the priest could fit this intransigent atheist's demands into his busy pastoral schedule.

> *The tram clattered by the Post Office; 'Now we come to the Immaculate Conception'; past the cinema: 'Our Lady"; the theatre: a sad slanting look towards 'The Private Secretary' (it was Christmas time.)*

Greene's exhaustively diligent biographer, Norman Sherry (to whom this essay is indebted) remarks that the play in question was not, in fact, the 1883 farce by Charles Hawtrey (no, not that one!) The panto at the Theatre Royal that year was *Goody Two Shoes*. But Greene might have better remembered a more appropriate production which did play during those few months in the winter of 1925/26: Shaw's *Saint Joan*, which he was to adapt for the movies thirty-two years later, with Otto Preminger at the helm and Jean Seberg at the stake.

Trollope (who, incidentally, retains to this day a reputation of particular skill in dealing with adult converts, in his ten years on Derby Road he received one hundred and fifty penitent converts into the church) had a hard job to convince this young man of an existence of a deity.

Greene was candid about his struggle: *'I fought and fought hard. It was like a fight for personal survival'*. But he was more circumspect about why he let the Hound of Heaven eventually track down his scent. To the end of his days he found belief in an anthropomorphic God untenable, but he had no problem with a more abstract possibility, something perhaps like Teilhard de Chardin's 'omega point.' Whatever it was Trollope said on those grimy Nottingham trams nevertheless eventually led to his solitary, typically Greene-land baptism, witnessed only by a *'woman who was dusting the chairs'*.

He made his confession, *'a humiliating ordeal... with that mixture of the feelings before a dentist's and the excited feelings before making a speech... Then I went on to the Nottingham Journal office and the football results and the evening of potato chips.'*

Greene took Thomas as his baptismal name. In his autobiography he is keen to make clear this was *'after Saint Thomas the Doubter and not Thomas Aquinas'*, after a cynic who had to see before he would believe, rather than after an intellectual dogmatist.

But maybe the choice of name was not quite so simple. At *A Celebration of the Life and Work of Graham Greene* at which I was present on International Writers' Day in 1992 (held, perhaps ironically, in the C. of E.'s Church House in the shadow of Westminster Abbey) Father Roderick Strange gave a talk on religion in the writer's work and pertinently reminded us that it was the disciple Thomas who said, following the raising of Lazurus and after the authorities had pronounced Jesus subversive, after the Son of Man had nonetheless made his existential decision to return to Jerusalem and certain death, it was the disciple Thomas who said: *'Let us also go, that we may die with Him.'*

Greene's retrospectively reticent act of faith confirms that after his conversion he remained very much the same man he was before it: a man unafraid of death; a man, indeed, socially, culturally, perhaps even congenitally bereft of the will to live; a man who described death as *'my heart's desire'*; a man who throughout his life perversely placed himself upon *'the dangerous edge of things'*; a man who seemed deliberately to court non-existence; a man who, so some say (and who could doubt them?) might almost have taken his own life had he not embraced a creed which deemed suicide a mortal sin; a man whose disgust with his own existence permeates those works of his which somehow make our existence more feasible; a man who lived well into his 80s.

*

It is time to return to the question of the use Graham Greene made of his short stay in Nottingham and to consider in some detail the only one of his novels which is set in Nottingham. Well, more or less set, because in *A Gun for Sale,* unusually for Greene, a real city is given a rather mythological transposition: the Nottingham of memory becomes the Nottwich of imagination.

A Gun for Sale was written during the final months of 1935 and the mood of the novel reflects those increasingly tense days. Greene wanted to write a 'hunted man' thriller, or 'shocker' as he referred to it, and he admits the influence of John Buchan's *Thirty-Nine Steps*. But his central character is no Richard Hannay, patriotically defending an Empire under threat: *'patriotism had lost its appeal, even for a schoolboy, at Passchendaele... the hunger marchers seemed more real than the politicians.'*

No, Raven is a hired killer with a hare-lip which is both an objective correlative of his twisted soul and a visible reason for an unfair world to despise him for a mark he was born with and can do nothing about: he is: *'a man out to revenge himself for all the dirty tricks of life, not to save his country.'*

In retrospect Greene was able to see that Raven was a prototype for Pinkie in *Brighton Rock* and, in many ways, Richard Attenborough's performance in that film is closer to the written Raven than any of the three screen incarnations.

> *'(Raven) is a Pinkie who has aged but not grown up. The Pinkies are the real Peter Pans—doomed to be juvenile for a lifetime. They have something of a fallen angel about them, a morality which once belonged to another place. The outlaw of justice always keeps in his heart the sense of justice outraged—his crimes have an excuse and yet he is pursued by the Others. The Others have committed worse crimes and flourish. The world is full of Others who wear the masks of Success, of a Happy Family... As children we have all suffered punishments for faults we have not committed, but the wound has soon healed. With Raven and Pinkie the wound never heals.'*

The other starting point was the then recent unsatisfactory white-washing parliamentary inquiry into the private manufacture and sale of armaments which exposed, but did nothing to curtail, the activities of the 'merchants of death'. In particular the exotic figure of Sir Basil Zaharoff, chief salesman for Vickers who trotted around the Balkan States selling tanks and missiles to both sides of any potential crisis, provided something of the inspiration for Sir Marcus, the shadowy figure in the novel who is the ultimate employer of Raven, and whose arms cartel has used Raven to assassinate a peace-loving European minister so that a war scare will make armaments share prices soar. Perhaps this is one reason why the story had to be set in a mythological town. The real Nottingham had none of the heavy industrial works of the story's climax; Vickers was, of course, based at Scotswood on Tyneside.

A Gun for Sale helped bail Greene out of his current financial difficulties as the film rights were sold to Paramount in May 1936 for an amazing 12,000 dollars even before the book was published. By the time it was filmed in 1941 the European war that Raven's act nearly precipitates and that his redemption forestalls, was already two years old in this country, and America was on the brink of entering the conflict. What had at the time of writing been speculative scenes of air-raid drill and domestic inadequacy in the face of total war had become an everyday reality in England.

The movie had the title under which Greene's novel had been published in the States, perhaps the more accurate *This Gun for Hire,* and was designed as a star vehicle for Veronica Lake with her policeman boyfriend (the Detective Sergeant Mather of the novel) played by Robert Preston. In the script by veteran hard-boiled writer W. R. Burnett (well-known as a writer of gangster pictures such as *Scarface, Little Caesar and High Sierra*) and up-and-coming Albert Maltz (now best remembered as one of the Hollywood Ten) Raven was to be, in the words of Quentin Falk who wrote *Travels in Greeneland – the Cinema of Graham Greene* (2000), *'a mere satellite to the top-credited couple, the cop and his girl'.*

Maltz later remembered the film as: *'a very creaky melodrama—in my opinion, pretty second rate. It doesn't stand up at all and I just don't know why it was so successful in the way it was.'* But one of those movie miracles happened. When the director, Frank Tuttle, viewed the first day's rushes, he was struck by the screen presence of the young unknown playing the hired gunsel in the shabby raincoat. The whole emphasis of the story was shifted to favour the character of Raven, played by Alan Ladd and in so doing the spirit of the film, in spite of the transposition of location from foggy East Midland streets to dark L.A. boulevards, remains spiritually close to the original.

Perhaps the film departs furthest from the novel in the depiction of the central female character, Ellen Graham, played by Veronica Lake. In the original this character is Anne Crowder, a none too bright hoofer for whom life upon the wicked stage has lost any allure it might once have had, and who has been hired as a last-minute chorus replacement for *Aladdin* at the Royal Theatre. Old Cecil Roberts would have once again done his nut at this wilful mis-remembering of the Nottingham Theatre Royal!

Anne has her prototype, incidentally, in the character of Coral Musker, another chorus-girl in the first of Greene's 'entertainments', *Stamboul Train*. On the damp quai at Ostend her mind goes back to more familiar surroundings: *'the electric signs flashing and changing over the theatre in Nottingham High Street. The stir of life, the passage of porters and paper-boys, recalled for a moment the goose-market, and to the memory of the market she clung, tried to externalize it in her mind, to build the bricks and lay the stalls.'* Anne responds to Raven's plight from a curious mixture of motives: at first it seems she is impelled by a desire to help her boyfriend's career, so that he might get promotion, marry her and take her out of all this. Later it seems as if an innate goodness motivates her to help remove that chink of ice lurking in Raven's soul. But all the time the reader might suspect she is collaborating in this dangerous adventure simply because it is more interesting than any life she's known hitherto.

In the movie, though, Veronica Lake is a classy cabaret singer cum magician who is recruited by the FBI.

Greene didn't think much to the picture. *'I've always wondered'* he remarked laconically, *'what happened to the cat.'* (If you've seen the film you may share that wonder—the stray Alan Ladd's Raven feeds in his hotel room seems to be there to endow the protagonist with a spark of feeling he doesn't extend to his fellow humans.)

This was one of Greene's novels which has been filmed more than once, but Greene never thought it worth the bother to check out the second version. Much time was spent tracking down what might well be the only extant print of the 1957 *Short Cut to Hell* for the Shots In The Dark Crime, Mystery and Thriller festival in 1992. I rather wonder whether it was worth such completist effort. But it has to be said it's a genuine rarity—James Cagney's only outing as a director (I wonder why?), one of the few films in which the director addresses the audience directly at the beginning of the picture to share his enthusiasm over the two young discoveries who play his leads only to promptly vanish from the history of cinema. Clearly the film is based much more directly on the previous screenplay than on the novel but keen eyes will notice that *This Gun for Hire* is here credited as the work of only Burnett... in 1957 the blacklisted Albert Maltz was still *persona non grata* in Hollywood, working sporadically under 'front' names.

The third version was a made-for-TV production of 1991 in which the action was transposed even further from Nottwich to New Orleans with Raven played by Robert Wagner—and of which the least said the better.

(Indulge a moment of bitter regret: my own protracted attempts to obtain the rights to produce an more authentic screenplay adaptation of the original came to nought. Such is life in an outhouse.)

Back to the novel: From Nottingham to Nottwich is a small step indeed. The story is set, realistically and symbolically, at Christmas—a time of promise in the imminent incarnation and, characteristically perhaps, a time of rotten weather:

> *There was no dawn that day in Nottwich. Fog lay over the city like a night sky with no stars. The air in the streets was clear. You have only to imagine it was night. The first tram crawled out of its shed and took the steel track towards the market. An old piece of newspaper blew up against the door of the Royal Theatre and flattened out... Along the line a signal lamp winked green in the dark day and the lit carriages drew slowly in past the cemetery, the glue factory, over the tidy cement-lined river. A bell began to ring from the Roman Catholic cathedral. A whistle blew.*

All his memories distilled into one paragraph. The river is re-named, incidentally and seedily, the Weevil, but I think from its geographical position and function in the tale it is more likely to be the Lean than the Trent.

Nottwich is a sink of municipal corruption with the town authorities and the local police force bought and manipulated by big business—power is mediated through the Masonic lodge. And yet it is on these mean streets, so easily transposed on film to the Los Angeles mean streets of the Hollywood *film noir,* that the sub-textual drama of the story is played out: the drama of

Raven's redemption. It is the seamless combination of the action/adventure story and the moral war fought over the salvation of a sinner's soul that makes this tale, like the later and greater *Brighton Rock*, so compelling.

*

The Catholic convert Greene could never bring himself to believe in Hell, and yet the drama of *A Gun for Sale* seems to be played out, if not exactly in the infernal regions themselves then at least in the suburbs of Hell. But its central characters, though unredeemed, are never irredeemable. For he did profess a belief in Purgatory, although he felt that it *'is something that may happen in this life.'*

Is it too far-fetched to suggest that, in this novelistic re-working, the by-ways of Nottingham have become the streets of Purgatory?

> *I don't know why a certain wry love of Nottingham lodged in my imagination.*
> *It was the furthest north I had ever been, the first strange city in which I had made*
> *a home, alone, without friends.*

Greene's memories of Nottingham certainly seem to have acquired a less jaundiced patina with age. When he arrived in London with the imminent prospect of seeing Vivien again he wrote: *'Thank God Nottingham's over. It's like coming back into real life again.'* But in an interview in the *Nottingham Evening Post* after the publication of the first volume of his biography, Norman Sherry rather movingly summed up the experience as follows:

> *He realised in Nottingham that he was a rather stuck up, superior middle-class*
> *boy who had been brought up to look down on all those rather dirty, untidy people*
> *below him.*

Quite. At one point he writes to Vivien, with a tone of voice so easily imaginable:

> *I don't think I'm a prig, but it is rather ghastly. One sees absolutely no one here of*
> *one's own class. In the street, in the cafés, anywhere. It destroys democratic feelings*
> *at birth.*

But something must have happened to him here in Nottingham. Sherry continues:

> *He changed his views and became an intellectual left-winger with a great deal of*
> *sympathy for people in need. He now looks back nostalgically to the days he was here.*

If our town has nothing else of which to be proud we can at least glory in the fact that we stopped Graham Greene from becoming Evelyn Waugh!

But there still remains that dystopic summary from his autobiography. with which this essay began. How was it that Nottingham was remembered? *'The focal point of failure, a place undisturbed by ambition, a place to be resigned to...'*

Ah yes, but we learn even more of the man when we persevere to the end of the sentence. If Nottingham is a paradigm of Purgatory, then perhaps Purgatory is also, for us sinners, what Nottingham became for Greene: *A Home from Home.*

DICKENS, GRIFFITH AND THE FILM YESTERDAY

Along with *Customs of the World* I also inherited from my paternal grandfather the complete works of Dickens. This edition is the 'Charles Dickens Library', published by The Educational Book Club Ltd. in 1910 which is distinguished by the copious illustrations by Harry Furniss. Furniss, also a lightning cartoonist and cinema pioneer most of whose films are now lost, could proudly boast that he was the only artist to illustrate the complete works of the Inimitable.

My first Dickens venture as a dramatist was a six-part TV adaptation of *The Pickwick Papers* to be produced by my dear comrade, Catherine Wearing, who had recently won awards for a splendid version of *Our Mutual Friend*. I jumped at the chance as I'd never seen any film or TV Pickwick that did justice to the original by being in any way funny. This is the favourite book of the great actor Timothy Spall—he had even chosen this to be taken with him onto that imaginary Desert Island—a true Londoner who was born to play the role, usually personated by a far too posh thespian. I first met Tim at the George Inn in Southwark, London's only surviving galleried tavern close to White Horse Yard where Samuel Pickwick met Sam Weller. When he asked me what my approach would be, I said 'I want to lay the ghost of Harry Secombe for ever', to which he replied 'I'm your man.' Catherine sadly died far too young and Tim and I have subsequently been trying to get the show off the page and on the road for the past two decades as the BBC bosses, in their lack of wisdom, canned the project, much to our rage and frustration. I did, however, manage to get a four-part radio adaptation commissioned with a splendid cast including Timothy Spall at the head.

Since then I have written two radio dramas of favourite works that had never previously been adapted: *George Silverman's Explanation*, a late and little-known masterpiece, and *The Bride's Chamber*, a convincingly chilling ghost story. In 2012, the bicentennial year of Dickens's birth, I wrote five biographical radio plays *The Special Correspondent For Posterity* about Dickens and London. And in 2016 I adapted *Great Expectations* for the stage of the (then) West Yorkshire Playhouse—a fine production directed by Lucy Bailey. As an aficionado of the recherché delights of early cinema I curated a DVD for the British Film Institute, *Dickens Before Sound*, a compilation of some of the silent versions of which about one hundred were made and about a third still survive, demonstrating the popularity of Dickens's stories and characters from the inception of cinema. This has led me to present film shows at Dickens events and conferences throughout the world, introducing Dickensians to the delights of the silent screen. Thank you, grandpa.

The following piece concerns *The Cricket On The Hearth*, the only film D.W. Griffith ever made from a Dickens source, perhaps surprisingly as he never resisted the opportunity to proclaim his indebtedness to the prose style of Dickens as a forerunner of his own development of cinematic language. My purpose was to expunge some of the misconceptions surrounding this short film of 1909 and to make the case for its originality as a masterpiece of adaptation from book to film.

*

The motto for this piece comes not from Dickens but Kipling:

> *I keep six honest serving-men*
> *(They taught me all I knew);*
> *Their names are What and Why and When*
> *And How and Where and Who.*

In the third paragraph of the third and, in its day, most popular Christmas Book, *The Cricket On The Hearth,* the genial, home-loving Narrator declares:

If I am to tell a story I must begin at the beginning.

Speaking from experience as an adapter of both works of fiction and 'true-life' stories into dramatic form, it seems to me that the greatest question always facing the writer is precisely: 'Where does the story begin?'

This story begins in the 1940s and resorts to flashbacks.

*

One of the most stimulating and influential essays on film—the way film works, the way film language developed historically, the way technical tropes of cinema bear ideological meaning—was written in 1944, towards the end of that brief period when the United States and the Soviet Union were allied in a common war effort.

In *Dickens, Griffith and The Film Today*[1] the great film artist and theorist Sergei Eisenstein traced what he called *'the "genetic" line of descent'* from Dickens's prose style to *'the American film aesthetic forever linked with the name of David Wark Griffith.'*

From all the works of the English writer he so much admired, Eisenstein chose, perhaps surprisingly, to begin his study at the beginning of *The Cricket On The Hearth.* In the 'close-up' of the singing kettle, 'intercut' with the chirping of the cricket in a humble setting, he finds a typical instance of 'Griffithesque' cinematic montage, creating a homely domestic 'atmosphere' which ultimately expresses *'the inner world and ethical countenance of the characters themselves.'*

It's not my purpose here to elaborate how Eisenstein developed his analysis of Dickens's prose as a precursor, a progenitor and, ultimately, as a limiter of cinematic language, nor how his necessarily survivalist conclusion stressed the

---

[1] Translated by Jay Leyda in *Film Form* Harcourt, Brace and World Inc. 1949. The title is, more literally: 'Dickens, Griffith and Ourselves.'

ideological superiority of Soviet cinema. I want to stick with the Cricket and let it sing unscrunched.

Eisenstein might well have seen the experimental play which remained in the repertoire of Stanislavski's First Studio of the Moscow Arts Theatre for many years after the Bolshevik Revolution—it was the last play Lenin saw shortly before his death and which he famously walked out of, damning its bourgeois sentimentality.[2]

The Moscow Arts Theatre Production

And perhaps he saw the film version of this production by Stanislavski's pupil Sulerjitsky, which featured Mikhail Chekhov and Maria Ouspenskaya (who both went on to have careers in Hollywood, perhaps more influential as teachers than actors).

But, though he mentions as an after-thought *'(o)ne of Griffith's earliest films was based on The Cricket On The Hearth'*, it is not very probable Eisenstein ever witnessed Griffith's one-reel adaptation of Dickens's Christmas Book.

If he had, he might very well have been disappointed at the lack of close-ups and switchbacks (parallel editing)—hallmarks of Griffith's more mature work which were to develop in his Biograph shorts well before *The Birth Of A Nation* (1914) and *Intolerance* (1917) let alone *Orphans Of The Storm* (1921) whose French Revolutionary setting possibly most reveals his debt to Dickens. However, Eisenstein's bracketed reference to Griffith's version of Dickens's tale became the subject of an editorial gloss by the distinguished film historian and expert on Russian cinema, Jay Leyda, who stated: *'This film followed the dramatic adaptation…made by Albert Smith with Dickens's approval'*, without unfortunately mentioning his source for this assertion.

My purpose is to question what is, literally, a footnote in film history in the hope of demonstrating that Griffith's film is anything but theatrical. Rather, this first adaptation of *The Cricket On The Hearth* for the cinematograph reveals so much about the transformation of prose fiction into film narration.

Griffith himself never hid the centrality of Dickens to his own dramatic practice—far from it. In *The Dickensian* of July 1922 the editor refers to a piece that had appeared in *The Times*:

> *Mister D. W. Griffith, the great film producer, has been telling Londoners how much he owes his success to Dickens. Dickens inspired him with an idea and his employers were horrified with it. "But" says Mr Griffith, "I went home, re-read one of Dickens's novels and came back next day to tell them they could either*

---

2 Nadezdha Krupskaya, *Reminiscences of Lenin by His Relatives,* Moscow 1956, pp. 201-07, available on the Internet as *Ilyich's Favourite Books* from the Workers Web project. On first seeing a rehearsal of Sulerjitski's production, Stanislavski declared that its theme was 'to awaken in people the sense of human-kindness.'

make use of my idea or dismiss me." And at a luncheon party of film producers…
he devoted himself to telling his audience what a great genius was Dickens… and
exhorting the audience to be proud of the heritage the great novelist left them.

Yet another version of this Myth of Origin appeared three years later with the publication of *When The Movies Were Young*, the memoir of Griffith's first wife, Linda Arvidsen[3]. In an oft-quoted passage whose possible lack of veracity has caused consternation among film scholars ever since, she also dramatises problems Griffith encountered with the prototype of the philistine Front Office. The disagreement occurred over *After Many Years*—the first of two films he made based on Tennyson's narrative poem *Enoch Arden* and, possibly the first script, or 'continuity' as they were then often called, written for Griffith by Frank Woods who most likely also scripted *The Cricket On The Hearth*. Vagueness, I'm afraid, comes with the territory.

After Many Years, although it had no "action"… proved to write more history
than any picture ever filmed and it brought an entirely new technique to the making
of films. It was the first movie without a chase…the first picture to have a
dramatic close-up, the first picture to have a cut-back. When Mr Griffith suggested
a scene showing Annie Lee waiting for her husband's return, to be followed by a
scene of Enoch cast away on a desert island, it was altogether too distracting.

'How can you tell a story jumping about like that?
The people won't know what it's about.'
'Well, doesn't Dickens write like that?"
'Yes, but that Dickens, that's novel writing; that's different."
"Oh, not so much, these are picture stories; not so different."
So he went his lonely way and did it…

When truth becomes a legend, print the legend.

The Cricket On The Hearth was the third of Dickens's Christmas Books, published in 1845. Perhaps the subtitle 'A Fairy Tale of Home' gives some indication why the tale is critically unregarded, as today's taste might consider this simple and broadly comic story of Domestic Harmony where Love Conquers All to be the acme of Victorian slush, playing into the hands of those who, like Trollope, consider Dickens to be 'Mister Popular Sentiment'. But in its day it was immensely successfully, selling, according to Dickens's friend and biographer John Forster and unbelievably to us, twice as many copies as *A Christmas Carol*.[4] In spite of the appearance of a life-size talking insect and dancing fairies, this is not a ghost story in the

---

3 Reprinted by Dover Publications Inc., 1969.

4 See Michael Slater's Introduction in *The Christmas Books, Volume 2,* Penguin English Library, 1971.

Daniel Maclise frontispiece and title page

mode of the Carol. For these supernatural elements might well be psychological emanations from the dozing fancy of the central character, John Peerybingle. They never attain the scary palpability (if that's the right word for spirits) of Scrooge's visitations.

Though the tale was adapted by Dickens himself as a Reading it could not have been a favourite of his as he only performed it four times: once on his second charity show in 1853 on December 29th in Birmingham, then on three subsequent occasions on his first professional tour of 1858 on April 29th and May 20th at Saint Martin's Hall, London, then finally at a matinee in Edinburgh on September 29th that year before it completely dropped out of his regular repertoire.[5]

Charles Foster Kent (really… not Kane!) in *Charles Dickens As A Reader* (published in 1872) wrote of *The Cricket On The Hearth*:

> *Throughout the chief part of the dreamy, dramatic little story, the various characters,*
> *it will be remembered, are involved in a mazy entanglement of cross purposes.*
> *Mystery sometimes, pathos often, terror for one brief interval, rose from the Reading*
> *of the Home Fairy-Tale.*

How is this 'mystery' organised in the original tale, which is split not into Chapters but 'Chirps'?

---

[5] Listed in Malcolm Andrews, *Charles Dickens and His Performing Selves—Dickens and the Public Readings*, OUP, 2006.

CHIRP THE FIRST is set on an evening in early January in the cottage where cheerful Dot is waiting for her older husband, John Peerybingle the carter. The first anniversary of their wedding is two days hence and their household also echoes with the sounds of their baby boy, their comic servant Tilly Slowboy, their dog Boxer and the eponymous Cricket whose hearthside chirping is a symbol of blissful domestic fortune, a constant presence since they first moved into the cottage.

Slow but honest John returns with his usual parcels for the villagers and, incitingly tonight, a mysterious and profoundly deaf Old Stranger he picked up on the cold road and who soon makes himself at home at the hearthside. Then they have a visitor in the shape of Caleb Plummer, the poor toy-maker who collects a

Richard Doyle: Chirp the First

package of dolls' eyes, ironic as they are never to be seen by his blind daughter Bertha. Perhaps things wouldn't have turned out so bad had not his beloved son Edward been lost at sea after setting out to make his fortune in the Golden South Americas. Caleb works for the next arrival: gruff old Tackleton, almost as misanthropic as Scrooge before his reformation, who has come to pick up his wedding cake. So now Dot is distressed to learn he is about to marry her beautiful friend, May Fielding. She feels sure her childhood chum must only be entering upon this union with reluctance because of her proud mother's reduced circumstances. For May once loved Ned Plummer—missing believed drowned.

The *dramatis personae* have all been paraded when something entirely out of the ordinary happens to turn the tale. As John deals with Tackleton's demands he hears Dot let out a sudden, uncharacteristic cry. Something has shocked his wife. Something to do with the Old Stranger. Something she refuses to share with her husband. What has his apparently faithful wife been up to?

At the end of the first part we readers know something is amiss but we have no more clue as to what shadow has fallen on the happy hearth than does John Peerybingle.

CHIRP THE SECOND takes place on the next day in the poverty-stricken home of dear Caleb Plummer. He has been duping his blind daughter to believe they live in some splendour and that really their employer is a jolly old soul who only pretends to be gruff for a lark. Implausibly taken in by her father's well-meant subterfuge Bertha continues to harbour an affection for Tackleton which only convinces him this blind girl must be a candidate for a strait-jacket. Now May and her mother, Mrs Fielding, enter and Dot's suspicions about May's reluctance to marry the old misery are confirmed. But still the presence of the Old Stranger seems to trouble Dot and she takes an opportunity to slope off with him secretly while the rest of the company play cards. Then all is

Chirp the Second

revealed... seemingly. For Tackleton takes great delight in leading John out back to show the honest carrier a shadow play of the Old Stranger flagrantly discarding his disguise and standing in a position of intimacy with Dot in his true colours as a handsome young fellow: *'Oh perfidious Wife!'*

At the end of the second part, therefore, we readers only know what John knows—though we might be not so inclined as John to jump to suspicious conclusions of Dot's seemingly adulterous betrayal.

CHIRP THE THIRD returns to John and Dot's cottage, where grief-worn Peerybingle undergoes his Dark Night of the Soul. Convinced, after Tackleton's prompting, that the young man must be *'some lover of her early choice'* jealous John takes down his gun. Will he? But then... Who should appear but the chirping Cricket *'in Fairy Form'*. With the aid of other Household Sprites conjured up from every domestic appliance, John becomes the spectator of moving pictures of his past life with the woman he has loved. Are these 'real' emanations or the product of John's turbulent brain?

Tackleton comes in on the third morning—the day he will be wedded to a younger woman, May, the day of John's wedding anniversary to another younger woman, Dot—expecting to find that John has performed violent

Chirp the Third

retribution. So his cold heart cannot understand why he discovers a husband far from obsessed with murderous vengeance but rather a thoughtful man who has decided to forego his own happiness for that of his young wife. Revenge has turned into Renunciation.

Are we as amazed as Dot is to overhear this sacrificial conversation? Are we side-tracked when Caleb enters to entreat Dot to tell Bertha about the lies he has told his daughter to cover up the truth of their miserable existence? The Final Revelation! At last Dot lets John in on what we might have suspected all along: This man is not some young lover but Ned Plummer back from the South Americas with gold in great store, disguised in order to determine whether his dear May really did want to plight her troth with the villain of the piece. At last we understand why Dot had to go against her own best nature to keep a secret from the husband she so loves for fear that the honest carrier would have blurted it out. Had she done so there would have been no further story to speak of.

Now we know everything, just as John knows and when he knows it. No more secrets, no more lies. A wedding, a dance, continual hearthside chirping. Even reformed Tackleton takes Mrs Fielding round her waist. Only poor blind Bertha cannot join the dancing couples—her role is to provide the tune on her harp. Merry Christmas and Gawd bless us everyone!

*

Of all Dickens's stories the tripartite structure of *The Cricket On The Hearth* most resembles the construction of the well-made three act theatrical drama: Inauguration; Complication; Resolution. Suspense; Surprise; Revelation. Put him in a tree; throw rocks at him; get him down from the tree. Could it be that this story was written with the theatre in mind? Hardly surprising as, in the days before authorial copyright, Dickens's books, from his earliest days and to his great distress, had always been subject to piratical adaptation:

Well, if the Pickwick has been the means of putting a few shillings into the vermin-eaten pockets of so miserable a creature, and has saved him from a workhouse or a jail, let him empty out his little pot of filth and welcome. I am quite content to have been the means of relieving him.[6]

Among the most tenacious of these theatrical thieving magpies was W.T. Moncrieff, immortalised beyond his talent as the original of a character who makes a brief appearance in *Nicholas Nickleby as* an un-named *'literary gentleman...who had dramatised in his time two hundred and forty-seven novels as fast as they had come out—sometimes faster than they had come out.'* Dickens uses his eponymous hero as a mouthpiece from which to spew out a torrent of his personal disgust:

(Y)ou drag within the magic circle of your dullness, subjects not at all adapted to the purposes of the stage... you take the uncompleted books of living authors fresh from their hands, wet from the press, cut, hack and carve them... hastily and crudely vamp up ideas not yet worked out by their original projector, do your utmost to anticipate his plot—all this without and against his will... to which you put your name as author... Now, show me the difference between such pilfering as this, and picking a man's pocket in the street.[7]

A decade into his literary career, however, Dickens got wise. He found a way to be to be in control of his own work.

For the first two Christmas Books, *A Christmas Carol* and *The Chimes*, he had personally sanctioned a theatrical version, so that at least one of the many in the competitive theatrical marketplace could claim authorial imprimatur, if only for a short time, if only for playbill hyperbole. But for his third seasonal entertainment Dickens went one better and did a financial deal with the Lyceum Theatre, run by a far more celebrated theatrical family than the Crummles: the Keeleys.

As an adolescent would-be thespian Dickens had taken acting lessons from Robert Keeley, whose wife, née Mary Ann Goward, subsequently became well known for her affecting depiction of Smike. The year before the Cricket chirped Robert had given his Trotty Veck in Dickens's second Christmas Book, *The Chimes*. But this would be the first time Dickens was to enter into a proper arrangement with theatrical management. This Christmas his story would be told exactly as he had conceived it. The conventions of the 19th century theatre would ensure that his novelistic descriptions could be realised by the Scenic Artist, and the internal thoughts Dickens gave to his characters would be presented through soliloquies and asides. The correspondent of 'The Almanack of the Month', 'W.H.W.' explained:

---

[6] From a letter of September 7, 1837, quoted in F. Dubrez Fawcett *Dickens the Dramatist*, W.H. Allen, 1952.

[7] Chapter LVIII.

That the Cricket might be served up quite warm to the play going public on the foyer of the Lyceum Theatre, its author—Mister Charles Dickens—supplied the dramatist, Mister Albert Smith, with proof-sheets hot from the press. On the evening of the morning, therefore, on which the book was published, its dramatic version was produced; and, as the adapter stuck very closely indeed to the text of the original, of course it succeeded.[8]

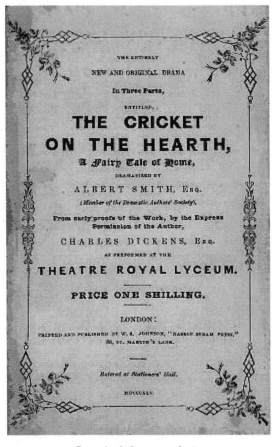

Poster for the Lyceum production

Though this production might be authentically promoted as the 'authorised version'[9], Dickens still did not receive royalties, merely a one-off payment for his license. But at least this sanctioned show pipped all other runners to the post. It was all of eleven days before the opening of the next contender at the Adelphi: a cut-down offering in only two chirps penned by theatrical stalwart Edward Stirling who had previously adapted the *Carol*. In this show, incidentally, Tilly Slowboy was played by a man, Edward Wright, well known as 'Jolly Ned' and not at all known for the restraint of his technique. This established a tradition that a part so ripe for comic business was often played in travesty by a 'dame'.

Soon, as Malcolm Morley put it: *'Of the two dozen theatres in town only some six were without the chirrup of a Cricket that Christmastide',*[10] There was even a production at the Haymarket, the 'West End version', which was, according to Morley, *'the first time any story from Dickens had graced its Theatre Royal boards.'* By the time

---

[8] Quoted in *The Dickens Companion* ed. J.A. Hammerton, , The Educational Book Co. Ltd. 1910.

[9] Albert Smith, *The Cricket On The Hearth*, Dick's Standard Plays No.394 n.d.

[10] Malcolm Morley, *'The Cricket' On the Stage* The Dickensian 48, 1952. Morley's series of articles about theatrical adaptations remain a valuable source, ripe for republication.

Smith's play opened in New York on the 21st February 1846, there had already been no fewer than twenty-one other productions mounted in Britain! S. J. Adair Fitzgerald wrote:

> *It is the most admirable proof of the popularity of Dickens with all classes to know that not only was the sale of The Cricket On The Hearth greater than that of any of the Christmas stories but its appeal to theatre-goers was irresistible.*[11]

And F. Dubrez Fawcett was certainly not overstating the case when he noted that:

> *Nothing like this furore has ever been known in theatrical history. It reached the high-water mark of the Dickens deluge... the real appeal lay in the aiders and the abettors of the plot... every part was "a piece of cake" for the performer.*[12]

Following the march-stealing premiere on December 20th, the Keeleys' Lyceum production returned after Christmas on a bill with *The Enchanted Horse—Prince Fironz Schah of Persia and the Princess of Bengal*—such were the surrealistic juxtapositions of the Victorian theatre—and the Cricket chirped into the new year for a total of sixty-one performances also sharing the bill with *Next Door* (a farce) and *Our New Governess* (a comedy).

As might be expected, Robert and Mary Ann Keeley cast themselves in the plum roles: Father was Caleb, Mother played Dot and their fifteen-year-old Infant Phenomenon, Mary, made her board-treading debut as Bertha. As might also be expected for this official version, Smith slavishly followed both dialogue and action of the story Dickens had permitted him to read before anyone else—this was less a case of adaptation than copying it out.[13]

Just as in the novel, the First Act (or Chirp) climaxes with Dot learning something about the Old Stranger, though neither John nor the audience share the knowledge:

> *Dot gives a loud shriek, starts up from her seat and remains transfixed with terror and surprise. Picture. Music.*

> JOHN: Dot... darling! What's the matter? Are you ill? What is it? Tell me, dear...! My own little wife—speak to me!

---

11 S. J. Adair Fitzgerald *Dickens and the Drama*, Chapman and Hall 1910.

12 Fawcett op.cit.

13 One insignificant change, however, is that the name 'Peerybingle' is transformed into 'Perrybingle'; though this might, of course, be a simple typographical error it is one which was, interestingly, later perpetuated in the Griffith film.

Stranger rises and stands—Dot falls into a fit of hysterical laughter, claps her hands together, and sinks upon the ground.

In the Second Act, stagecraft is precisely described for that moment of John's complete sight of, and total misinterpretation of, his wife's apparent act of betrayal:

> *The Stranger, who has been exchanging looks with Dot, gets up unperceived and goes towards door Left. Dot appears anxious to follow him as he beckons to her. This is through the dialogue... Dot has taken a candle from the table, timidly, and followed the Stranger. The light is seen directly afterwards behind the blind of the large window... When it becomes stationary Tackleton advances and lays his hand upon John's shoulder... Tackleton advancing to the window draws back the blind... The window looks into a warehouse, now lighted, in which are seen Dot and the Stranger, as a young man, with his arm around her waist—she takes his white wig and laughs as she puts it on his head.*

At the start of the final chirp, comes the apotheosis of the Spirit of the Cricket and the Household Nymphs (impersonated by a dozen children)—a spectacle which plays like a Movie of Memory in John's troubled brain:

> *John bursts into tears and sits down again by the fireside. Music continued. The hearth opens and the Fairy Cricket is seen, covered with filmy gray veil. The Cricket keeps chirping but faintly, so as not to interfere with the dialogue... As the Fairy Cricket finishes speaking, the chimney above the mantelpiece opens slowly and discovers a tableau-vivant—a facsimile view of the interior of the cottage with a miniature figure of Dot, sitting by the fireside, as in Act 1st, Tilly Slowboy, Baby etc. At the same time troops of small Fairies appear from every available position; some forming a sort of border to the tableaux, others run to John and pull him by the skirts, to call attention to the picture... The Music becomes louder and hurried. A film descends in front of the tableau. The scene becomes darker and a shadow appears to obscure it. The Fairies express consternation and strive to rub it out or put it on one side. When it goes away it discovers Dot sitting by the side of the cradle, with her hands clapped on her forehead and her hair hanging down. The Fairies get round her, kiss her, and try and fondle her.*

So the play not only follows the story exactly but also animates Daniel Maclise's frontispiece illustration. Could Smith and the Keeleys have had prior access to the pictures as well as the text? And might Dickens himself have deliberately created these improbable images to satisfy the mid-century's fascination for stage fairies?

The response of the public and the reviews of the critics recognised the uniqueness of this production. *'It is long since we have witnessed such enthusiasm as that evinced by the audience upon the fall of the curtain.'* (The Illustrated London News).

'The drama is full of broad humanities—there is an utter absence of class feeling—all prejudices, all distinctions are merged in one gushing flood of benevolence.' (*The Morning Post*). And *The Times* applauded an adaptation which was produced *'under circumstances entirely new… The audience… far from coming to see a dramatic illustration of a work already read, for the most part derived their knowledge of the book from witnessing the drama.'* This review also speculated perceptively *'that the book was not only written for the stage in general, but also for the particular company of the Lyceum.'*

Perhaps Dickens really did have the particular skills of the Keeleys in mind when he crafted characters which their talents seem to have so ably impersonated.

Of the many other metropolitan productions from this time I've only thus far had the patience to track down one where the authorial credit is given to 'Anon', though this is most likely the version by W. Thompson Townsend which opened on the 5th of January at the City of London in Bishopsgate, a theatre specialising in *'domestic and temperance melodrama'* sharing the stage with, amongst others on a quadruple bill, *Harlequin, King Lud of Ludgate*. This is an altogether cruder piece than Smith's with far less elaborate stagecraft. The original dialogue is flattened out and interpersonal complications are made more explicit. Townsend presumed to improve on the Inimitable's already not too subtle humour, as when the hard-of-hearing Old Stranger mis-hears 'Tilly Slowboy' as 'Silly Snowball'; and when Caleb is asked if he is busy he replies: *There's a slight gallop on rocking horses.'* But the important fact is that the way the mystery is revealed remains exactly the same as in Dickens's original and Smith's authorised adaptation.[14]

Could it really have been Albert Smith's version, which followed so straightforwardly if no doubt so professionally the narrative organisation of the original source, upon which Griffith's film was based as Jay Leyda confidently asserted? Sure enough, Smith's play was constantly revived throughout the east coast of the United States during the 1890s and might well have been seen by Griffith. There is, however, another version of the *Cricket* which may well have a stronger claim for inspiration of the Biograph film.

*

Dot opened at the Winter Garden Theatre in New York on September 14th 1859 and was the one of the more than one hundred and seventy plays authored by Dionysius Lardner Boucicault. This premiere featured the famous comedian Joseph Jefferson (later especially noted as Rip Van Winkle) as Caleb and Agnes Robertson (then Missis Boucicault) as the now eponymous heroine. She was *'distinguished by… delicate artistic perception and polished execution'*.

Incidentally, Dion Boucicault was an older man who had entirely lived up to the reputation of life upon the wicked stage by his scandalous second marriage to this young woman so maybe the December/May marriage at the

---

[14] Available from The Victorian Plays Project, victorian.worc.ac.uk.

centre of the story held a personal resonance? In his biography of the always prolific and occasionally great Irish dramatist Richard Fawkes says Boucicault claimed never to have read the Dickens novella, but based his version upon one of the many extant dramas.[15] When *Dot* finally crossed the Atlantic *The Athenaeum* was surely correct in the notice of the 19th of April 1862:

> *His version differs from preceding adaptations by the adapter's dealing freely and dramatically with the story and thus avoiding that obscurity and mystery which, in its original state, were calculated to puzzle rather than please an audience.*

Once again, that word 'mystery'.

In the first London production another Keeley daughter, Louise, played Dot and John Lawrence Toole played Caleb, a part which was taken by Henry Irving in a revival later in the decade. *The Examiner* for the 19th of April 1862 commented that Toole's performance as the blind toymaker was the chief attraction of the Adelphi production:

> *Best of all is the Caleb Plummer of Mr Toole, which is a piece of really good acting, in which none of the pathos of the part is either sacrificed or caricatured, while every touch of Mr Dickens' genial humour that still clings to it in the dramatic version is well re-produced. Mr Toole's Caleb Plummer is an advance upon everything he has yet done above the range of burlesque and farce.[16]*

And from *The Illustrated London News* (19th of April, 1862, p. 393.):

> *New scenery of the most beautiful and complex kind has been painted for the piece by Mr T. Grieve, and is of such rare excellence as to form of itself a sufficient attraction. But the play is also capitally performed. The Dot of Miss Louise Keeley is perfectly charming, and the Bertha of Miss Simms a fine piece of artistic acting. Then there are Miss Woolgar in Tilly Slowboy and Mrs Marsten in Mrs Fielding, while Mr Toole and Mr Emery leave nothing to wish for in Caleb Plummer and John Peerybingle. Mr Billington is lively and effective in Ned Plummer and Mr Stephenson, in Tackleton, as disagreeable as could be desired... There can be no doubt that Mr Boucicault has given to the stage a version of this famous story which will last as long as boards are boards.[17]*

When the curtain opened any audience familiar with previous theatrical versions might well have been bamboozled by Boucicault's idiosyncratic approach. For the first characters who appear in 'A Wood' are hardly

---

[15] Richard Fawkes, *Dion Boucicault*, Quartet Books Limited 1975.

[16] Quoted in H. Philip Bolton, *Dickens Dramatized,* Mansell Publishing Ltd., 1987.

[17] Bolton, op.cit.

Dickensian: it's Oberon and Titania from *A Midsummer Night's Dream* summoning up Ariel and Puck![18]

The King of the Shadows sadly declares:

My faithful ones, sad remnant of the past
Of all the ancient fairies we're the last...

Ariel agrees:

We're not believed in...

Because there's a new fairy who represents the modern world:

My Name is Home...
O'er all the household Elves I hold command,
My Home the chimney corner, my Scepter this
A Knitting Needle, emblem of Cheerfulness...
My Merry Elves,
Come from your Cozy Nooks and Shew yourselves.
Kettle, Cradle...
And now my little Cricket, quick come forth;
Leave for awhile your corner on the hearth...
Behold the Elfin Band
That rule the modern realms of fairyland.

(I may not be alone in finding this theatrical sentiment reminiscent of a most resonant first paragraph concerning the death of now-abandoned deities in a stupendous book which was published in the same year as *Dot* opened in London and of which Boucicault could surely not have been aware: *La Sorcière* by Jules Michelet:

There are authors who assure us that a little while before the final victory of
Christianity a mysterious voice was heard along the shores of the Ægean Sea,
proclaiming: 'Great Pan is dead!' The old universal god of Nature is no more.
Great the jubilation; it was fancied that, Nature being defunct, Temptation was
dead too. Storm-tossed for so many years, the human soul was to enjoy peace at last.
Was it simply a question of the termination of the ancient worship, the defeat of the
old faith, the eclipse of time-honoured religious forms? No! it was more than this.
Consulting the earliest Christian monuments, we find in every line the hope
expressed, that Nature is to disappear and life die out—in a word, that the end of
the world is at hand. The game is up for the gods of life, who have so long kept up

---

[18] Text available from The Victorian Web, www.victorianweb.org.

44

a vain simulacrum of vitality. Their world is falling round them in crumbling ruin.
All is swallowed up in nothingness: 'Great Pan is dead!'[19]

Well, perhaps I may be alone!)

In Boucicault's play the Olympian Orders enter into an arm-wrestling dialectic with the Domestic Deities to set up the theme of his drama: The War Between the Old and the New Gods. And while this argument evolves there's a parenthetical image for the spectator's confusion:

Wood opens: Edward Plummer discovered asleep on Mast of Ship.

Whence comes this tantalising tableau? From what narrative time? Could it be: 'Once…' a flashback? Or is it: 'Meanwhile…' happening at this very moment but somewhere else? But maybe it's: 'And Then…' what takes place next? Or even, though unlikely: 'Perhaps…' a future foretelling? Whatever, the figure of someone whose identity we don't yet know now has been palpably foreshadowed.

Adding further spice to an already well-seasoned pot, Boucicault peppers his Prologue with another ingredient deliberately resonant of Shakespeare: the hubristic vice of Jealousy. For Titania declares: *'Othello o'er again!'* But The Cricket challenges Oberon by championing the unassuming hero John Peerybingle:

We'll see/ Who shows the nobler heart, the Moor or he.

As a consummate Man Of The Theatre Dion Boucicault must have realised that, a dozen years after publication, the popular Dickens story had long since become old hat. The twist in the tale—the Third Chirp revelation that Old Geezer is really Young Hero—had been let out so often as to eliminate any possibility of anticipation or surprise. He had to come up with an original plot organisation which still allowed him to tell the old, old story, to exploit the audience's desire to revisit well-loved characters, to wallow again in the dear, sentimental theme.

Though the original three-day time scheme remains the same, the Choreography of Knowledge (who knows what, when, why and how?) is deftly and radically rejigged. Structurally, there are only three possible options for the writer in dealing with the relationship between protagonist and reader/spectator in regard to what is known: (i) the audience can know exactly what the protagonist knows, no more no less; (ii) the audience can know less than the protagonist knows; or (iii) the audience can know more than the protagonist knows. In Dickens's story, of course, the reader only knows what John knows when he knows it. But in *Dot* it is the third of the above options—where the

---

19 Jules Michelet, *La Sorcière*, Paris, 1862, translated in 1939 by Alfred Richard Allinson as *The Sorceress*.

audience knows more than the central character—which is how Boucicault decided to adapt the original. This serves to shift the dominant role from John to Dot, his title character.

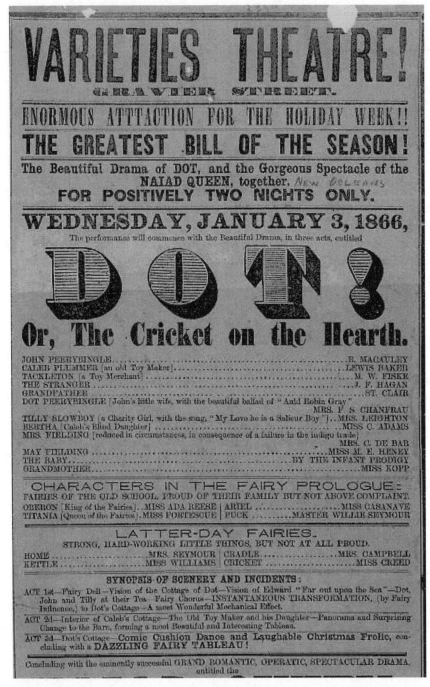

Dot in New Orleans

In Hitchcockian terms such knowledge which the audience possesses has, but which the character(s) doesn't/don't is what constitutes Suspense[20]. In *Dot* it's up front right near the start of the First Act when the audience learns, at the same moment as Dot learns, that the Mysterious Stranger is really: *'Your own Ned come back again'* to claim his love. So that's the chap we saw asleep on the ship! Now the audience also learns, as Dot learns, why Edward Plummer will not allow her to let her darling husband in on the subterfuge:

DOT: Don't ask me to have a secret from John.

EDWARD: Only for one day, and for my heart's sake… John is too honest to keep my secret… And you will promise that you will not betray it to May until I prove her heart is the same as I left it. If you refuse I'm off to sea again.

If Dot were to tell John what she knows, and what the audience now knows with her, she would ruin everything because there would be no more story.

In this sprightly, innovative adaptation, the audience's focus is completely shifted onto Iago Tackleton's temptation of Othello John. Will the husband mistrust his innocent young wife? Will he murder the disguised man he wrongly believes to be her lover but who Dot knows, and we know with her, to be Ned returned from the sea? Theatrical conventions had developed since Albert Smith's day. No longer any need for asides when the dramatic situation has been laid out with sufficient clarity. Dancing insects are entirely redundant when the gods are watching.

Dot was by far the most popular version of *The Cricket On The Hearth* in the United States. Malcolm Morley reckoned it must have played in *'every playhouse in English-speaking America'*, although, perhaps unsurprisingly, provincial tours usually dispensed with Oberon and Titania in the Prologue.

There exists a playbill for a production of Smith's old adaptation in Brooklyn in 1896, in which Joseph Jefferson seems to have jumped ship. So if there really was a theatrical source for Griffith's American picture for Biograph it's surely Boucicault's *Dot* which would have been the most likely candidate.

*

It still seems baffling that, given the ubiquity of Dickens adaptations in the first two decades of cinema, as well as so many previous Magic Lantern presentations, D.W. Griffith made only one film based on a work of the writer whom he continued to claim had directly influenced his patented film style.[21]

[20] Hitchcock outlines his classic delineation of the differences between 'suspense' and 'shock' in Francois Truffaut, *Hitchcock by Truffaut*, (London, Martin Secker and Warburg, 1968) p. 91

Given its theatrical popularity throughout the 19th century, however, perhaps it's not so strange that the sole chosen work was *The Cricket On The Hearth*.

The film was shot in three non-consecutive days, April 8th, 18th and 24th, 1909, in the American Biograph Company's studios on 14th Street in downtown Manhattan and on location in Fort Lee, New Jersey.[22]

Sure enough, just as Dickens's tale might be little read and less regarded these days, oft dismissed as one of The Inimitable's more cloying offerings, Griffith's film (amazingly the one hundred and tenth one-reeler he had made since he began to work for Biograph less than a year before!) is rarely acknowledged as one of his most significant contributions to the developing language of cinema. Nevertheless, we now might see through a paper-print darkly that this film may well represent a crucial shift in the history of story-telling adaptation from prose fiction to cinematic narration which entirely leap-frogged over previous theatrical presentations.

While so many other films from the early days are missing believed lost, most of the Biograph productions are still extant because 'paper prints' were fortuitously lodged for copyright protection at The Library of Congress. Though copies subsequently struck from these amazing survivals can never entirely replicate what must have been the pictorial beauty of the originals (shot in this instance by Arthur Marvin and Billy Bitzer), the productions are equally privileged in film history because *The Biograph Bulletin* was issued to accompany every release. *The Cricket On The Hearth* was featured in Number 243 on the film's release in (appropriately) May, headlined BEAUTIFUL ADAPTATION OF DICKENS' FAMOUS STORY.

Though this in-house periodical confidently drummed: *'The story is so well known to everyone that it would be useless to dwell at any great length on it,'* it nevertheless felt the need to go on to delineate in some detail the exposition of the film's narrative. Perhaps this précis was written for the benefit of a Lecturer, a live cinematic interpreter about whose role little is known but who was in those days sometimes employed to help decipher shadows on the screen for a poor, often illiterate audience unfamiliar with the original novella?[23] But even more educated

---

[21] The only other direct Dickensian quotation in a Griffith film comes from *Brutality* made in 1912, where a violent husband repents his ways upon seeing Nancy's murder by Bill Sikes in a theatrical adaptation of *Oliver Twist*—a narrative device he had already employed in *A Drunkard's Reformation* of April 1909 in which a drunken father sees the error of his ways when he takes his young daughter to the theatre to see a naturalistic Zola play. So life upon the wicked stage does have redeeming social value after all.

[22] Information from Tom Gunning, *D.W. Griffith and the Origins of American Narrative Film—the Early Years At Biograph*, University of Illinois Press, 1994 & *The Griffith Project, Volume 2*, General Editor Paolo Cherchi Usai, bfi Publishing/Le Giornate del Cinema Muto 1998, which includes *The Biograph Bulletin* and a commentary by Scott Simmon.

[23] Certainly the five intertitles are not exactly illuminating. They are absent from the print in the National Film and TV Archive and were reconstructed, based on

patrons with prior knowledge of the literary source or, more likely, one of the many stage shows derived from it, might still have had some difficulty in following the entirely modern approach of this cinematic version.

What is it that makes this old brew in a new wineskin so remarkable?

In the film, running for about sixteen minutes depending upon projection speed and inclusion of intertitles, the story is told in only twenty-five shots, though, as Scott Simmon has remarked: *'it feels like more because the shot length is so varied.'*

SCENE ONE: INT. THE PLUMMER HOUSEHOLD.

TITLE: *Edward Goes to Sea.*

Setting the start of the story in this place and at this time is already a departure from any previous telling. Dressed as a sailor young Edward Plummer (Owen Moore) bids farewell to his father, Caleb, an old toymaker who is so poor he dresses in a sack-cloth jacket (David Miles) his blind sister, Bertha (Dorothy West?) and Dot (played by Linda Arvidsen, Griffith's then wife, whose not always reliable memoirs have been so influential in their assertion of Griffith's debt to Dickens). Edward swings his kit bag over his shoulder and strides away. In this version, though not in the original story, *The Biograph Bulletin* indicates that Dot is Edward's sister though nothing in the title or mise-en-scène gives any indication of the relationship between these four characters.

TITLE: *His sweetheart.*

SCENE TWO: EXT. LANE.

Edward bids a fond farewell to his sweetheart, May Fielding (Violet Mersereau). They embrace and he's off, leaving her alone in the frame to hope and wait for his return. Though she has put on a brave face in his presence, her gestures and countenance indicate her sadness at his departure.

---

information supplied by Graham Petrie author of *Silent Film Adaptations of Dickens* in The Dickensian, Nos. 455/6/7, 2001/2, for the version available on *Dickens Before Sound* double dvd (bfi Film and Video 2006; Producer: Caroline Millar; Original Music: Neil Brand; Compiler: Michael Eaton).

SCENE THREE: INT. PLUMMER HOUSEHOLD.

Back in Caleb's house, the old man gives his blessing to the betrothal of Dot—so clearly she must be his daughter—to John Peerybingle (Herbert Prior), a big, gangly, slow, lumbering fellow, much older than his betrothed but evidently honest as the day is long and with a kind heart. They kiss and Caleb bestows his blessing by shaking his toys as if they were ritual objects. His poverty-stricken condition is reinforced, as 'Glass Handle With Care' can be seen on the back of his make-do jacket.

SCENE FOUR: INT. FIELDING HOUSE.

When the rich, well-dressed grouch, Tackleton (Harry Solter) visits Mrs Fielding (Anita Hendrie) waving a bill, it is clear that she has, according to *The Biograph Bulletin*, *'gotten into moderate straits'*. He goes out... then almost instantly returns (as if this were possibly two scenes originally to be separated by a title?). Clearly his dastardly plan is that only May's hand in marriage will clear the debt. Her mother willingly agrees and pleads with her unwilling daughter. Tackleton's frown and his consultation of an account book indicates the dire consequences should his desire be thwarted. So, resist as she might, May is callously pushed into the arms of the old misanthrope by Mrs Fielding and Tackleton embraces her. *The Biograph Bulletin* comments: *'Of course this is repugnant to May, whose heart is for Edward.'*

These are all, of course, backstory incidents in the original Christmas Book—only to be revealed to the reader much later. Never before depicted. Never before dramatised. *'I must begin at the beginning.'*

But where should this story start? When Edward decided to venture to sea on a long-shot mission to make his fortune? When Dot decided to wed an older man and they moved into their cottage and first heard the chirping of the cricket, symbol of domestic bliss? Maybe even earlier, when Caleb became poor? Or when Mrs Fielding's long-dead husband lost his wealth? What a variety of decisions storytellers have to negotiate when they inaugurate their yarns!

TITLE: *Three years later. Edward's return. He finds his sweetheart May betrothed to Old Tackleton.*

SCENE FIVE: EXT. KING GEORGE INN.

This is not a location Dickens ever thought of using! What follows is the boldest expositional departure in the adaptation from original story book to screen. Four Customers are smoking and talking outside the inn when Edward returns, still in his sailor suit with his coat over his shoulder. He pats a dog at a wayside inn and goes inside for refreshment.

Would the film be readable without the intertitle's minimal amount of information? Would an audience know of such a temporal shift without this title, lost to most future generations in the extant paper print? Would the words of a Lecturer apprised of the précis in *The Biograph Bulletin* have made sense of this crucial location? No previous theatrical version had employed such a significant structural and temporal change as this. Whose story is this? Right now, it seems as if it is Edward who is the Protagonist embarking upon the narrative's journey, for he will be the character who learns the terrible knowledge which inaugurates the problem of the Second Act.

SCENE SIX: INT. KING GEORGE INN.

Again, not a scene Dickens thought needed writing! Yet it is crucial to the way Griffith chose to tell this tale. Inside the tavern Edward looks happy, the Barman is at the back of the set (notice the Biograph trademark literally stamping its copyright seal onto the scenery) and another Customer is up front right of screen. As Edward picks up his tankard the Barkeep comes forward, counting on his fingers perhaps to indicate an event to take place in a few days' time? Literate spectators would already know from the title what Edward is about to find out—the viewer is one step ahead of the character in the Choreography of Knowledge. Two Women enter in the foreground... it's getting pretty crowded in the King George Inn. Edward listens, only to infer with horror that they must be gossiping about his own true love, joking of his beloved's impending marriage to an old man everybody in these parts detests. *The Biograph Bulletin* spells out the awful realisation: *"He learns of the impending nuptials of Tackleton and May."*

SCENE SEVEN: EXT. KING GEORGE INN.

Edward rushes outside, desperate.

SCENE EIGHT: EXT. LANE.

Edward secretes himself to see old Tackleton proudly walking out with May, chaperoned by her mother. Using an idiom of performance appropriate to the time Edward makes his distraught feelings more than evident, putting his hand on his heart as he witnesses Tackleton, characteristically self-important, chucking May's chin. He follows them off, out of frame right.

SCENE NINE: EXT. WOODLAND PATH.

Edward continues to follow the three of them as they walk up the path and exit close past the camera. When they have left he hangs his head and beats his brow. Yes, it must be true! (A costume historian might be able to date the fashions, which seem to an untutored eye to be contemporary for the men but old-fashioned for the women—doubtless purloined from Biograph's costume closet.)

SCENE TEN: INT. KING GEORGE INN. LATER.

A saddened Edward comes back into the inn and slumps at a table where a Barmaid serves him with a tankard. Enter a figure whose over-sized, eccentric features are instantly recognisable to later generations. It's none other than Mack Sennett cutting his cinematic teeth as part of the Biograph rep company. Actually, he's not the 'Merry Andrew' *The Biograph Bulletin* credits, for this is another clownish figure in white-face like Joey Grimaldi who prances in the background plucking a mandolin. Sennet's character must be a Travelling Player in a fairground show which just happens to be in town for he takes off his top-hat, dons a white wig and strikes a theatrical pose. This is another necessary invention, absent from any previous version, whose introduction serves to raise Edward's spirits and assist him in his quest. Seeing him, Edward has a light-bulb moment and a grey wig is helpfully at hand for him to put on. Merry Andrew continues to entertain as Edward and the Showman go off screen left. They all too immediately return and now the young man is decked out as an old man. At last a nagging question Dickens never thought to ask is finally answered: Where did he get his false beard and his old man's disguise? The actor produces a mirror to show Edward his new look and he seems pleased—no-one will know him. Clearly, his masquerade will enable him to discover May's true intentions.

SCENE ELEVEN: EXT. KING GEORGE INN.

In a long shot, Edward, now stumping along in his costume as the Old Stranger, walks away from the inn. The cart of the Carrier enters frame left and finally John Perrybingle (sic) is introduced as he pulls up to hand out packages to the folk outside the inn. Edward has another sudden great notion and cadges a ride with the man who in this telling is his brother-in-law—though John, of course, does not know this.

SCENE TWELVE: EXT. PEERYBINGLE'S HOUSE.

John's cart pulls up outside a wood-framed house and a supernumerary makes his only appearance to stable the no-longer-needed horse. John helps the Old Wayfarer down, still entirely unaware of his guest's true identity under the false beard. It is not winter, there is no snow on the ground; it is not evening, but broad April New Jersey daylight— though it is possible some prints may have used a blue filter to signify night-time.

SCENE THIRTEEN: INT. DOT AND JOHN'S PARLOUR.

Finally the appearance of Dot, in the studio set of the Peerybingle's happy home, as she watches over her baby in the foregrounded cradle with her comic nursemaid, Tilly Slowboy. Perhaps to Griffith's credit, nothing much is made of this role, often much expanded past endurance in previous theatrical adaptations. The titular hearth is prominent on the right of the screen and could that be a barely noticed Chekovian pistol hanging over it? (*'If in the first act you have hung a pistol on the wall, then in the following one it should be fired. Otherwise don't put it there.'* That's the rule!) But obviously no kettle is whistling, no cricket is chirping. Dot looks outside of the window, excited at her husband's immanent return. John comes into the happy home, warmly embraces his young wife, goes over to his baby's cradle before pointing outside, remembering his agèd passenger.

And now after more than a third of the way into the film, this is where Dickens's story starts, where the two modes of telling finally coincide.

But the privileged access to backstory events which the original writer only revealed at the very climax of his tale means that the film's spectator sits in a completely different relationship to the characters from that of the reader, who was placed in the same state of ignorance as John Peerybingle vis-à-vis the true identity of the mysterious visitor. Indeed, it might even be said that the spectator is witnessing a different story, one whose central problematic focuses on Edward Plummer and his quest to stop May from marrying December.

This long sequence shot in the parlour continues as John comes back in and introduces the Old Stranger—remember we know, before Dot even suspects, that he is really her brother Edward. Tilly pulls the cradle out of the way as its up-front position would now be too distracting. The Stranger walks towards the glowing fireside—which quite possibly would have been coloured with a red filter—and is led by May to a comfy chair at the front right side of the hearth. Perhaps an original print less grey and washed-out than the paper simulacrum, which so fortunately survives, would have revealed through her facial expression that May already suspects something as she brings the visitor a warming cup. Now Tackleton arrives with May and her mother, Mrs Fielding, to be followed by Peerybingle who leads in blind Bertha. Seeing his family so reduced Edward can barely keep up his pretence and drops his cup and saucer. May approaches… but is pulled away by Tackleton. When Dot goes over to clear up the mess Edward takes the opportunity secretly to reveal himself and mimes his intention to discover whether his sweetheart really has transferred her affections to this rich, elderly miser. With no-one else watching Dot leads him off into an adjoining room, away from the hearth, where that ominous gun might be glimpsed.

CUT AWAY TO:

SCENE FOURTEEN: INT. BEDROOM.

In the bedroom Edward takes off his hat, abandons his elderly gait and looks at Dot whose returning look seems to convey that May has not stopped loving him.

CUT BACK TO:

SCENE FIFTEEN: INT. PARLOUR. AS BEFORE.

At the parlour hearthside, malicious old Tackleton listens at the door before going to collar the Carrier. John opens the bedroom door and is shocked at what he espies.

CUT AWAY TO:

SCENE SIXTEEN: INT. BEDROOM. AS BEFORE.

In the bedroom the false beard is removed to reveal what the spectator already knows and what Dot suspects. This is not an old man but a sprightly handsome youth who holds out his arms and embraces John's wife!

CUT BACK TO:

SCENE SEVENTEEN: INT. PARLOUR. AS BEFORE.

John cannot believe his eyes as he turns back to the triumphant Tackleton who has provoked this troubling revelation.

An insurmountable problem with the mise-en-scène? In the book John sees the couple only from a distance and in silhouette, so there's no chance he could recognise the features of a young man whom he knew so well before his departure. In the film, however, it is surely stretching credibility that John doesn't spot that the man with his wife is really Edward. The differing narrative structures of the book and the film both demand John to assume this disguised stranger is a secret lover of Dot, shrouding clouds of doubt over his erstwhile happy marriage. Readers of Dickens's story must surely be convinced that there must be some innocent explanation, not yet imparted. John's jealous suspicions must surely be completely delusional, though at this point they know no more than he does.

At last the problematic of the film shifts, merging with that of the story. No longer is the anxiety: *'What will Edward do?'* at the forefront of our minds. Now the question of the tale is: *'How will John react?'* And, having already been let in on what John doesn't know, the structure shifts to what might be elaborated as Hitchcockian Suspense. Or, more basically, the pantomimic: *'He's behind you!'* Stitched into John's predicament, we are desperate to reveal the truth to him, to prevent the potentially tragic consequences of his mis-seeing.

John is overcome with jealousy, wanting to go back to confront the couple, but May distracts him just as Dot comes back in through the bedroom door and goes over to say goodbye to May and the others. Before he leaves Tackleton collars John, waving his stick to urge him on to violent revenge, whilst behind him his loving wife is taking down his pipe from the mantelpiece. In a fine performance, John morosely slumps down upon the chair, unable to face either the hearth or his devoted wife. Dot leaves him, uncomprehending. For she, too, does not know what we know, what the camera's eye, differently selective from the writer's quill, has chosen to reveal.

A candle flickers on the table. John stands and walks over to the door… and stops as his eyes look up to see the pistol hanging over the domestic hearth. If we had somehow failed to notice it before, now the full significance of this object is framed by his hands. He takes it down, looks at it, cocks it and walks away from the hearth nearly knocking over the fire-irons—a presumably unintended piece of business the actor consummately rectifies, dispelling any need to re-shoot the whole of this lengthy, elaborately-blocked, narratively-crucial scene. John looks up the stairs to check Dot is not around, determinedly waves the gun in the air and opens the bedroom door… *(Don't do it, John! How could you doubt her? If you only knew what we know, what she knows!)* Then he stops and drops the weapon on the floor. Chekov be damned! Break the tragic rule! To commit a crime, even one of passion, is against this character's tender nature. John picks up the candle and snuffs it out. Suddenly the lighting pattern changes, noticeable even in the lack of contrast in the paper print. This scene would have once looked glowingly wonderful and we can but imagine. Lit only by the glow of the fire in the cricket-less hearth, John slumps on the mantelpiece before almost collapsing, head in hand, to begin his long, lonely vigil.

Throughout this central scene both the expression of emotion through action and gesture from the ensemble in general and John in particular, coupled with the elaboration of narrative through inter-cutting between the two adjoining spaces, has been nothing less than superb. If this print were not already so far from its original monochromatic splendour and so particularly degraded at this very point, the complex use of light to convey interior mood could be appreciated in all its glory.

John Peerybingle's Dark Night of the Soul represents the most fundamental transposition from Novel via Theatre into Film. Griffith and Frank E. Woods, if he was indeed the Scenarist, adapted the story into a (chrono)logical linear cause and effect plot without eliminating any of the main characters—except, of course, for that guardian of household contentment, the Cricket. Refusing to give palpable form to the metaphor which gives the tale its title, the film chooses to depict both Edward's quest and John's existential anxiety entirely naturalistically.

Though Biograph at this time were never known for their reliance upon 'special effects', this aesthetic purity cannot have been a simple technical or budgetary exigency. It is not hard to imagine what Meliès or Pathé might have done with this scene—there might have been a troupe of female dancing insects with revealing legs and fluttering wings even more beautifully coloured than in any stage version. It's doubtful even that R.W. Paul, who seven years before in the very first days of the kinematograph had produced with former stage magician Walter Booth in his North London studio the earliest extant film adaptation from a Dickensian source in *Scrooge, Or Marley's Ghost,* which made ample use of photographic tricks for flying spirits and the superimposition of the past upon the present, could have resisted the temptation to kit out some hapless performer as an Actual Cricket.

TITLE: *Next morning. The cricket hushed. John's self-sacrifice. 'I am old. She is young. Why stand in her way?'*

The only mention of the eponymous bug comes in this now missing intertitle, which is redundant if not meaningless in Griffith's version. This is the only line of dialogue, in case the lesson of forgiveness has not yet been driven home.

SCENE EIGHTEEN: INT. BEDROOM. NEXT MORNING.

Before the mirror, Edward again dons his disguise. Now his purposeful objective is to prevent May from marrying a man he knows she despises.

SCENE NINETEEN: EXT. PEERYBINGLE'S HOUSE.

Dot creeps to the gate, looking very cagey until the apparent Old Man comes across to join her in cahoots. John watches in despair as they leave together in apparent merriment. His suspicions of cuckoldry seem to be confirmed and he raises his fist, his anger not completely abated. Then he collapses on the gate post, resigned to his wife's desertion.

TITLE: *May's wedding day to Old Tackleton. A surprise.*

SCENE TWENTY—INT. FIELDING HOUSE.

This is another scene Dickens never thought of writing but obligatory to this version.

May weeps at the thought of her loveless wedding as her unyielding mother peers out of the window. It's Dot who comes in and Mrs Fielding parades her unhappy daughter in her bridal finery, before the heartless mother returns to the window, evidently expecting the arrival of the rich, old bridegroom-to-be. Dot seizes this opportunity to share the revelation to May in a silent stage-whisper. Miming some hard-to-decipher pretext concerning the wedding gown, Dot persuades Mrs Fielding to enter an inner room off screen… And as soon as she's in Dot turns the lock on the old lady. May slumps back, hiding her face on the table, until Dot ushers in the Old Stranger. He instantly pulls off his, truth be told, never too convincing wig and beard. Dot has to turn her gaze away as the True Lovers embrace, reunited. But May displays her bridal gown: What is to be done? Never short of a notion, Edward's resolving finger waves and the three conspirators rush out.

SCENE TWENTY ONE: INT. DOT AND JOHN'S PARLOUR. MORNING.

Poor John, whose ignorance now annoys less than his toleration cheers, packs a bag, preparing to leave… until on the table he sees his dear wife's handkerchief. He lifts it to his face and breathes in her scent. This little scrap of white cloth, so deliberately reminiscent of *Othello*, provides a far more realistic objective correlative of a once happy hearthside than any supernatural insect. Griffith, like Tackleton, has scrunched the Cricket, whilst preserving its metaphorical import.

SCENE TWENTY TWO: EXT. OUT IN THE WORLD.

Back on location outdoors in New Jersey, Edward, Dot and May rush into the frame. Fortunately, there's always a *deus ex machina* Minister around when needed (Arthur Johnson). Overcoming a momentary reluctance, the ritual specialist grasps the hands of the young folks, persuading a conveniently passing Pedestrian to act as a legally sanctioned witness—which is what we have been all along. A solemn, hats-off moment as the two lovers are joined in holy wedlock on the public highway. Phew! Edward has at last accomplished what he set out to do.

SCENE TWENTY THREE: INT. FIELDING HOUSE.

The door opens and the curtains blow as old Tackleton, dressed in his bridegroom finery, enters the house of his young bride-to-be proudly carrying a bouquet. He has increasingly become a laughable caricature, a *commedia del arte* Pantaloon whose role is to have his desires thwarted. Presumably he hears banging noises, which we cannot, emanating from off screen right, for he opens the door to free the indebted mother of his supposed bride-to-be and his puffed up chest soon deflates. Blaming the old woman, the bridal bouquet becomes a convenient prop with which to clobber her over the head.

SCENE TWENTY FOUR: EXT. OUT IN THE WORLD. AS BEFORE.

The improvised yet binding ceremony is over. Edward and May are Husband and Wife. Youth has conquered Age. Spring has triumphed over Winter. But as they embrace, Tackleton rushes up and attempts to prevent the marriage. Too late. His garland becomes even more bedraggled when used to wallop the Minister. Edward's problem is solved, his story resolved.

But what about John? All eyes on the finish!

SCENE TWENTY FIVE: INT. PARLOUR. AS BEFORE.

Back in the Peerybingle parlour, where so much of this story has taken place, John has his bag in hand, resigned and determined to leave for good or ill. Then Dot returns screen left, amazed to find him leaving. As the wife looks perplexed the husband answers by pointing towards the bedroom door. The penny drops… Dot can't help turning away and laughing. Wait! She goes off and brings in the Happy Couple, at a stroke clearing up the misunderstanding without which there could not have been a story.

The Mystery Guest was a brother, not a lover!

Now John recognises Edward, though he's hardly nearer than when he first peeked into the bedroom. *The Biograph Bulletin* expresses collective relief: '*Well, John discovers what a fool he has been in doubting Dot.*'

John is distraught at his suspicions: How could he have doubted his wife? Dot effects to be angry but finds it hard to keep up the pretence and Old Husband and Young Wife embrace as the, thankfully minor character, Tilly Slowboy makes her entrance with their baby—emblem of their conjugal union. From nowhere old Caleb and blind Bertha enter the scene to be reunited at last with the sailor son.

As in the original, every character must be brought back on stage for the finale. So Tackleton enters from the farthest left edge of frame, excluded from the others whose arms are all locked in a ring. Given what it has been through the bouquet he carries seems unfeasibly less bedraggled. Even Tackleton uncharacteristically finds it in his heart to forgive. Did he ever have a character or was he just a necessary co-ordinate on the narrative grid? What does it matter? For he warmly shakes Edward's hand and then suddenly he is approached by Bertha. Out of nowhere, perhaps another betrothal can't be far off—a possibility never envisaged by Dickens who had implied it could be the more age-appropriate Mrs Fielding who might well find a future with the reformed gruff Tackleton. Now everyone knows everything.

The film concludes, like the original story, with misunderstandings revealed and problems resolved, a last-minute, all-but-instantaneous conversion of the gruff villain, betrothals all round, the restoration of domestic harmony and the ultimate reconciliation of Winter and Spring.

The only two words writers enjoy writing: THE END.

*

Six honest serving men: Who knows What, Where, When, How and Why? Not just another way of ordering well-known incidents but an entirely novel Choreography of Knowledge, it is difficult to accept that Biograph's *Cricket On The Hearth* was 'based upon' any previous theatrical adaptation.

If I am to tell a story I must begin at the beginning.

So soon it's Cinema.

JAMES CAGNEY

During the 1990s and early 2000s I wrote a regular column and the occasional feature for the monthly *Sight & Sound,* published by the British Film Institute. Among these were profiles of film actors and these are two of my favourites: James Cagney and Robert Mitchum. Both began their careers as contract players under the financially lucrative but artistically restricted studio system—Cagney with Warner Brothers in the 1930s, Mitchum with RKO in the following decade. Both kicked against the pricks—Cagney by setting up his own independent productions in the hope of securing more creative control, Mitchum by putting up a protective curtain of whisky fumes and dope smoke between himself and anyone who dared to tell him what to do. Both began as rebels... and ended as Republicans. But the best of their work, and their embodiment of two different species of the twentieth century male, still deserves to be relished long after the white heat of the films in which they appeared seems to have come from out of the past.

James Cagney

*

Jim Cagney (only Hollywood publicists ever called him 'Jimmy') was born in 1899, died in 1986 and his was a life of The American Century. In *Cagney* by John McCabe (Aurum Press, 1998) the reader learns that his father, James senior, was a saloon keeper with Irish roots from New York's dirt poor East Side, everybody's friend and darling of his children, who took fifty nips of whiskey every day to keep him sweet until he started having 'fits' and unsurprisingly died too young. His mother was of Norwegian stock and came to be known in the neighbourhood as Kill-'Em Carrie because she once took a bullwhip to a night-watchman who had beaten up one of her boys. She lived to see two of those boys become wealthy doctors, her only daughter become an actress, and the third of her sons become the business manager of his brother, the greatest male movie star of the early Golden Age of sound cinema.

Cagney never lost that street grace derived from two of his most regular activities on the streets of Yorkville: dancing and fighting. Early photographs show that his face had the gravitas of a grown man when he was but a kid, and in old age his face still carries the lost innocence of childhood. When he played gangsters he moved like a hoofer and in musicals his body moved with the taut, efficient control of a street-corner pugilist. In Busby Berkeley's *Footlight Parade* (1933) he dances on a bar to 'Shanghai Lil' as if his life depended on it: 'his arms free-floating and in total consonance with the lithe movements of his body.' In *Angels With Dirty Faces* (1938), directed by Michael Curtiz, he plays a pimp, Rocky, with such pizzazz that it is never any wonder why the Dead End Kids would choose him as a role model over Pat O'Brien's pious priest. As McCabe puts it: 'he stood with his arms down and his fists pressed against his abdomen, then lifted his fists in a constant hitching motion, usually accompanied by a roll of his shoulders.' So hard to describe, so impossible to forget. Rocky's catch-phrase, "Whadda ya hear? Whadda ya say?" is delivered in that unmistakeable machine gun rat-a-tat which turns a greeting into a clubbing. When he was asked by his instructor in the Student Army Training Corps—a German professor name of Mankiewicz, father of Herman and Joseph—where he learned to talk so quickly he answered: 'Upper East Side, sir. That's where you learn to walk fast, talk fast, think fast—and run fast.'

In spite of these inauspicious beginnings he was filled with an almost obsessive desire to learn from his surroundings. A loner as a child who never allowed himself to get sucked into the pack, he was known until his dying day by O'Brien, one of his best friends, as 'The Faraway Fella'. He soon graduated from amateur dramatics to chorus boy and met the chorine who would become his partner for life, Willie Vernon. If his beginnings might have been imagined by Eugene O'Neill then this is more than appropriate as O'Neill was a member of a theatrical syndicate which gave him a leg up into the legitimate theatre, and in 1930 he was offered a contract by Warner Brothers.

Jack Warner and James Cagney had nicknames for one another. The studio head called his crowd-pulling star, who won himself a permanent place in the hearts of the American public when he pushed half a grapefruit in Mae Clark's kisser in *The Public Enemy* (1931): 'The Professional Against-er'. Cagney called the tight-wad mogul 'The Shvontz'—Yiddish for 'prick'. Cagney always knew that, however well rewarded, he was still a proletarian, a hired hand, to be forced into one churn-'em-out under-budgeted picture after another with no say over his roles, his career, his image. However much money they made the Warners never lost the small businessman's fear of the work force. Cagney would deliberately screw up scenes and refuse to work late on studio pictures with a three-week turnaround prolonging the agony as he knew that the crew were employed on a daily rate. On more than one occasion he walked out of his contract and into the law courts, threatening to go to medical school, to retire to the land or establish his own independent production company to produce films that few would see because the big boys had distribution tightly sewn up. But each time he walked back into Warner Brothers his brother Bill would have managed to secure him a massive salary hike.

Cagney's natural solidarity was with his fellow performers, the writers and the cinematographers whose crafts he could understand and admire. For the most part he despised directors, dismissing them as talentless kiss-ass wannabes: 'Direction is implicit in the writing, and if you've got a good script, competent actors, and a fine cameraman you barely need a director.' Mervyn LeRoy comes in for a particular dose of vitriol: 'Just before the action began—but the camera rolling mind you—he'd stroll into camera range, talk briefly to us actors with shit like "Now, boys and girls, I want you to give me your best in this. Lots of pepper." Why? Because he knew damned well the dailies would be seen by the big shots…(and) he would come out looking as if he had been responsible for the whole thing.'

Few other great directors were spared: Anatole Litvak was a German dictator too proud to eat with his crew; John Ford was past his best by the time he directed Cagney in *What Price Glory?* (1952) and was drinking so heavily while helming *Mister Roberts* (1955) that he had to be replaced with the hated LeRoy; Billy Wilder broke the spirit of the ageing thespian during the shooting of *One, Two, Three* by insisting upon every nuance of line delivery and, in one instance, pushing until the fifty-seventh take before he was satisfied.

The kind of directors Cagney worked best with were the ones who left him alone: Raoul Walsh, who directed him in one of his most popular films of the 30's, *The Roaring Twenties* (1939), and in 1949 in his greatest role of all as the psychotic Oedipal mother-fixated Cody Jarrett in *White Heat* (a part which seems to be more a commentary on his earlier performances as a gangster rather than a simple reprise of them) seems to have been content to allow Cagney and his co-stars to work out their own business while he got on with choreographing the action. Michael Curtiz came in for some grudging respect, when he directed Cagney in one of the great show-biz bio-pics *Yankee Doodle Dandy* (1942), a model of boiled-down cinematic story-telling, over and above its sentimental patriotism appropriate to the year after Pearl Harbor, based (very loosely as usual) upon the life of George M. Cohan. This was a part Cagney was born to play: 'Mike was a pompous bastard… but he sure as hell knew how to treat a camera…He left me alone because he knew I'd knock him on his ass if he didn't… A bright man. Intelligent. Yet he never learned one of life's—and art's—basic rules: be good to your actors, and they'll be good to you.'

No need to even speculate what Cagney's response to the auteur theory would have been, but his approach to his own craft can be boiled down to one pithy homily: 'Just do it!' It's an intuitive, street-wise, even osmotic philosophy which reflects his own entry into the profession. When asked by a reporter: 'How do you get to be an actor?' his reply was: 'Just become one. Don't sit around thinking about it. Do anything that will let you stick around a theatre so you can soak it up.' This credo, however, entirely fails to explain why he was so damned good at it.

Cagney was the first to recognise that there was something of himself in all his roles. His was a talent that was forged on those Yorkville streets before the First World War, his characters always seem to look back nostalgically to a world he had already lost by the time he was playing them. He was by every account a complete actor, a generous actor, whose work, though looking so spontaneous, was the product of hours of meticulous preparation before he entered the studio gates. What gives his work such lasting charm and force is the underlying feeling of insouciance—that he could, at any moment, shrug his shoulders and leave a profession often characterised in the public mind as full of snobbery and pretension without a second thought. Always entirely himself he is also, somehow, one of us.

Though best remembered as a hoodlum in what he termed 'cuff operas' he played gangsters in only about a quarter of his sixty-four film roles—who recalls him as a doctor, a dentist (!) or an insurance salesman? According to Cagney the trick to embodying the bad guy is 'to get solidly on the side of the guy you're playing', even the psychotic Cody Jarrett: 'He was bright... to himself he was doing absolutely the right thing.' Maybe that's why Norman Mailer said: 'Cagney was a gut fighter who was as tough as they come, and yet in nearly all the movies he made you always had the feeling that this is a very decent guy. That's what we all want. There's nothing more depressing than finding a guy as tough as nails and mean as dirt.'

James Cagney lived a long life surrounded to the end by the showbiz cronies and the wife he loved. In most respects he was a happy and fulfilled man who reaped considerable material rewards and universal recognition while preserving a professional generosity. A man with few skeletons in his closet he could always be relied upon to put meat on the bare bones of any part he was given to play. He was a man whose many interests outside the business meant that he was never obsessive and monomaniacal about something he considered to be just a job, albeit one he laboured at with consummate and unrivalled skill. His rags-to-riches life, his relentless yet seemingly effortless rise through Vaudeville via Broadway to Hollywood could only have been lived in the United States of the twentieth century.

Even his personal politics seem to reflect a general American trend. The quotidian penury of his background and the exploitative working conditions of his profession engendered an early liberal, if not outright socialistic, set of values. His generous contributions to striking Mexican agriculturists in the 1930s came back to haunt him when the self-serving Dies Committee—precursor of the red-baiting HUAC—came looking for headlines through communist smears. It was crucial for him to play the part of 'the biggest flag waver in show business' in *Yankee Doodle Dandy* to wash off the dirt which still stuck to his name. The war compounded his lifelong patriotism which veered ever closer to Republicanism, and by the time he died he was a substantial property owner and Nixon supporter. Once again the lie is given to Scott Fitzgerald's pessimistic—and, one suspects, solipsistic—formulation that there are no second acts in American lives. Maybe I've misunderstood something—I always thought that the *raison d'être* of California was to allow the adoption of as many serial identities as its wilfully amnesiac denizens desire.

So why is it that this biography, written by a man who ghost-wrote Cagney's blandly uninformative autobiography, who knew him very well and admired him more, and who is himself an actor who has an evident sympathy for the nuances of the craft, is, ultimately, so depressing? Is it because so many of these films are now forgotten? Or is it more the saddening realisation that perhaps so many of them deserve to be? Of course, every film which has Cagney's name above the title is worth seeing but often only for his performance. Even Cagney himself refused to see most of his pictures. He couldn't bear the memory of the penny-pinching, never mind the quality feel the width values of Jack Warner who never felt any need to nurture and expand his money-machine's career and who regarded Cagney only as that awkward 'against-er' who refused to toe the line. Slogging through the inventory of all those Warner Brother pictures of the 30s it is impossible not to feel that that his legacy is a simulacrum of what might have been, that the studio system which made James Cagney also betrayed him. And in betraying his talent they also cynically betrayed the aspirations of their audiences.

ROBERT MITCHUM

According to the official biography put out by RKO Radio Pictures, Robert Mitchum was a child vaudeville performer who wandered in South America before graduating from Duke University. But this was a farrago of fabrications by studio publicists to add an air of exotic allure to their new contract player. They needn't have bothered. The truth as recounted in the excellent *Robert Mitchum—Baby I Don't Care* by Lee Server (Faber, 2001) was far more fascinating.

After his father was crushed to death in a horrific accident when his son was barely two, the young lad was dragged up by the family of his bohemian mother. By the

Robert Mitchum

age of seven young Bob was a published poet with local celebrity. But he was always a mischievous kid with a wide streak of malice and was expelled from school when he shat in a teacher's hat. His first apocryphal visit to a theatre was when a strip-tease artiste sneaked him into Minsky's Burlesque House beneath her voluminous fur coat under which she was sporting only the pelt she was born in. 'Any boyhood visions of growing up to be a policeman collapsed right there.'

At fourteen he ran away from home to ride the boxcars as one of the Wild Boys of the Road. 'I guess my ambition was to be a bum.' Drifting between trains he acquired a life-long taste for 'poor man's whisky', the marijuana that grew tall and free at the side of the tracks, but he later supplemented the rich man's variety to this quotidian habit. Somewhere along the road he also picked up a propensity for reciting Shakespearean soliloquies by heart. He escaped from a chain gang in the Georgia swamps but the suppurating ulcer caused by the friction of the shackles nearly caused a leg to be sawn off. Finally fetching up in California he picked up a few dollars and a broken schnozz on the semi-pro boxing circuit. He started to hang around the fringes of the trade union movement and somehow found himself in an amateur theatre group. Describing himself as a 'conditional communist', he even wrote a play about a militant labour boss called *Fellow Traveler*—an interesting tit-bit for this writer as I scripted a film with the same title.

Scratching a precarious living writing jive spiel for cabaret artistes his break in pictures came as a rep player in a series of Hopalong Cassidy six-reelers: 'Free lunch, a hundred dollars a week and all the manure you could carry home.' The second of these dirt-cheap horse operas, *Border Patrol* (1943), was penned by future blacklistee, Michael Wilson, and concerned ol' Hoppy breaking up a forced migrant labour racket organised by a wealthy despot. Those McCarthyite anti-red zealots were not far wrong when they accused pinko scribes of smuggling commie propaganda into routine oaters. Before long Mitchum had secured a contract with RKO, then under the control of Charles Koerner, who was determined to make the studio profitable by eschewing art such as *Citizen Kane* in favour of popular entertainment. But it was soon to be taken over by obsessive-compulsive multi-millionaire air-ace erotomaniac weirdo, Howard Hughes.

Bob was initially exempted from military service in WW2 on physical grounds (false teeth, no less!) and was first really noticed as an actor of stature playing a fictional soldier in *The Story of G.I. Joe* (1945), an early instance of the world-weary role which he would continue to play throughout his career. He was, however, eventually conscripted into the infantry towards the end of the war as an alternative to penal servitude after he decked a couple of L.A.'s Finest who'd made the mistake of trying to run him in for drunkenness. He never saw the kind of front-line combat he fought before the camera but achieved martial honours as one of the 'keister police', a medical orderly performing rectal examinations on newly conscripted men—a 'poop chute inspector' as he delicately put it.

And then, in 1947, almost back to back, came three defining roles in films whose reputation should be assured forever in movie history. Raoul Walsh, monocular helmer of the western *Pursued*, made no attempt to figure out screenwriter Niven Busch's structure derived from Greek tragedy nor the script's over-wrought Freudianism. *Out of the Past*'s already complicated flashback plotting was not made any more comprehensible when several expository scenes got lost *en route* from the mimeo machine and aesthetician Jacques Tourneur's complex visual symbolism was stymied by the exigencies of RKO's legendary stinginess. At the time neither of these films were considered any great shakes or set the box office tills on fire and the term *film noir* had yet to be been coined by Paris cinephiles. Retrospective appreciation is an instance of later critical discourse triumphing over industry standards of judgement. We now recognise them both as far more cinematic than the Academy's worthy but yawn-inducing choice for best picture that year, *Gentleman's Agreement.*

Crossfire, however, was different. Made in twenty days, it was another no-frills picture shot on down-beat, thread-bare sets at a budget of $250,000. Adapted from a novel which took as its theme prejudice against homosexuality among a group of returning veterans, screenwriter John Paxton, producer Adrian Scott and director Edward Dmytryk decided that this was far too risqué and shunted the subject matter towards another form of bigotry: anti-Semitism. The brilliant combination, maybe even confrontation, of a serious social message content with a skew-whiff, low-key, gloomy form which hinted at a deeper and more pervasive existential dread made this film a massive success, taking $1,270,000 profit and earning it a Best Picture nomination.

By the time the name of Kazan's well-lit, heart-on-the-sleeve movie dealing with the same social problem had been taken out of the Academy envelope, however, Dmytryk, Paxton and Scott had already been hauled before the House Committee on Un-American Affairs and *Crossfire* was being touted as the (allow me) *'cine qua non'* to raise the wrath of Washington's red-baiters against those so-called cosmopolitan intellectuals who stoked the motion picture machine.

Mitchum, as usual, claimed only to have memorised his lines and looked moody. He could perceive nothing in common between himself and the 'swimming pool Stalinists' of Hollywood. But he was and would remain, though now a big star, temperamentally connected to the dispossessed outsiders among whom he had spent his shuffling days and who were never denied a billet in *su casa*. On the only occasion when his long-suffering wife persuaded him to see a head-shrinker, the eminent Doctor Frederick Hacker came to the psychoanalytic conclusion: 'You suffer from a state of over-amiability... failure to please everyone creates a condition of self-reproach.'

Perhaps it was this predilection for insouciant amiability that led to the incident for which Mitchum will be forever known even by those who have never seen him in one of his classic roles. When two undercover policemen crashed into a Laurel Canyon bungalow they found Mitchum and a pal sharing, with a couple of bottle-blonde starlets, a pakolola of gage—as hipsters like Mitch would have called a 'marijuana cigarette'. The whole scene stenched of set-up. When cuffed and asked his occupation the movie star replied: 'Former actor.' He was eventually sentenced to two years probation, sixty days of which were to be spent in jail. Most of the stretch was spent in the penal farm at Castiac north of the city: 'like Palm Springs without the riff-raff.'

Any other Hollywood reputation might have been tarnished beyond redemption, but Bob's fan base (including his jail-bait posse, the Droolettes) had always responded to the whiff of sulphur he exuded. With Hughes's support and clandestine surveillance, his spell as a guest of the County only seemed to enhance his charisma, though Ike would never permit a screening of any of his films in the White House during his presidency.

Mitchum had written home during his rambling days: 'Trouble lies in sullen pools along the road I've taken'. And he later declared that: 'All life is spent in obeisance to the Id.' Well, maybe because of the early death of his father (pardon the mobilisation of the thought-system of *Pursued*) Mitchum does seem to have possessed a spectacularly under-developed Superego.

Inevitably, much of the account of his last forty years does make depressing reading. His bred-in-the-bone misogyny, his driven infidelity, his surprising and shocking occasional casual racism and even, in his later years, his purported espousal of crazed secret-government conspiracy theories might, perhaps, be blamed upon his corrosively self-destructive drunkenness. Many friends and colleagues continue to assert that these malign personality traits should be seen as a 'Contrarian's' need to shock and leave confusion in his Trickster's wake rather than as expressions of sincerely held beliefs of which he was incapable— contradictory chinks in the armour-plate of an antediluvian masculine armour rusting under the continual water torture of changing societal values. (He would have loved that analysis!)

Nevertheless, throughout his life he always had the ability to reappear and remodel himself in yet another terrific defining role. I am not alone in finding his portrayal as Reverend Harry Powell in *Night of the Hunter* (1955) a particularly chilling favourite. The never to be forgotten moment comes when the murderous demonic preacher emerges from the night to stalk the children and creepily croons the evangelical hymn 'Leaning On The Everlasting Arms'. The children's protectress, Lillian Gish, cut from the same cultural cloth but on the side of the angels, begins to harmonise the chorus from the porch of her shack: '*Lean on Jesus... Lean on Jesus...*' Over and above Laughton's consciously Griffith resonances, is there a starker and more melodramatically believable delineation of fictional Love and Hate, Good and Evil anywhere outside of Dickens?

But there are so many other memorable performances. Not entirely arbitrarily: from the 50s there was the past-it, saddle-sore, rodeo-rider in *The Lusty Men* (1952); from the 60s Hawks's *El Dorado* (1967), where he looks like he's actually enjoying himself for once (we even learn that Duke Wayne wouldn't turn down a toke of his buddy's ubiquitous spliff); from the 70s his anti-heroic, small-time loser in *The Friends Of Eddie Coyle* (1973) and the unmannered elegy to his own trench-coated past playing Chandler's Philip Marlowe in *Farewell My Lovely* (1975); from the 80s... well, perhaps best draw a veil, but in the 90s, two years before his death, a short but blazing appearance as the embodiment of pure malice in Jim Jarmusch's post-modernist western *Dead Man* (1995).

And then there are the ones that got away: the Clark Gable part in *The Misfits*, Pike Bishop in *The Wild Bunch*, unforgettably played by William Holden; the Burt Lancaster role in *Atlantic City* (Louis Malle was shocked when he saw the face-lift!) and Popeye Doyle in *The French Connection*, a role he rejected because he couldn't bring himself to portray a drug-busting cop—it's hard to imagine him chasing the drug baron with anything like the energy embodied in Gene Hackman's breath-taking performance. Mitchum never seemed to care and was usually far too drunk or stoned to regret some spectacularly idiosyncratic career moves. His choice seems to have been motivated more by the location than by the quality of the project. He told one young actor: 'The movie business has been like a magic carpet for me'—words which must have stuck in his craw when he was mired for months on the west coast of Ireland in *Ryan's Daughter* (1970), possibly his most miscast performance whose auteur, David Lean, worked, according to Server, 'at the speed of a pyramid builder'.

Throughout his long career Mitchum never failed to affect a disdain for his profession: 'like plumbing… with more makeup,'; his roles: 'I have two acting styles, with or without a horse,' and his films: 'gorilla pictures', pounded for ten reels then 'in the last shot you get the girl and fade into the sunset'. Working with George Peppard on Vincent Minnelli's *Home From The Hill* (1960) the young Actors' Studio acolyte asked the jaded pro if he'd studied the Stanislavsky Method… the reply was that he was an adept of the Smirnoff Method.

So what was it that made this untrained actor such a spectacularly dangerous screen presence? Lee Server talks of his air of 'majestic… ineffable cool… (his) stoicism, grace under fire, wry unflappability in the face of life's ever-threatening absurdities'. In the biographer's memorable phrase he was 'a man who could easily not bother to put on his second sock.' But the camera, as they say, loved him. Many a time some sideliner from the front office would nervously witness a take and wonder what exactly it was this property did to justify such a massive above-the-line salary, only to be shocked to see a performance of such great power, subtlety, beauty and truth when the dailies rolled.

Clearly Lee Server loves his subject, but this admiration never spills over into mindless idolatry. Mitchum's persona, on and off screen, takes us close to the core of a certain species of 20th century American masculinity that he at first embodied and then later out-lived. Confronting him, on and off screen, involves facing a heart of darkness and a personal sky as big and ultimately as lonely as that of the western landscape.

Are we able to get any closer to penetrating the secret of this iconic enigma and his mythic journey from Log Cabin to Winnebago? If not, this is no fault of a meticulously researched, briskly written book by a writer whose crisp prose style and snappy construction indicates that he would have thrived in Rancho Broke-O when the pulps were hitting the news stands. Like his subject Server hides his erudition and, yes, his wisdom, producing one of the finest and most troubling show-biz biographies I've read in many a long year.

Mitchum's Life and Art—a word that secret poet would only ever have employed to rhyme with flatulence—cannot but help make us ponder hard upon the magnificent monstrousness of movie mega-stardom. Martin Scorsese, cinephile as well as cinéaste, when signing Bob up for a cameo in the remake of another one of his high spots *Cape Fear* (1991, the original was released in 1962), proudly told the actor he had seen all one hundred and three of his movies. 'Beats me', came Mitchum's retort, 'I've seen about seven.'

BLIGHTED MY LIFE—BILLY MERSON.

My maternal grand-mother, Annie Maddison, hailed from Notintone Place in Sneinton, also the birthplace of William Booth, the founder of the Salvation Army—perhaps an inappropriate name for an evangelical dispensation which continues to rely upon the mellifluous tones of brass bands as literal instruments of conversion. But the greatest legacy I inherited from her was not religious. Rather it was her love of the repertoire of the Music Halls which she would share with me when I was but a child and the knowledge of which has sustained me throughout my life well into the present century when they have been all but forgotten. One of our favourite songs was *The Spaniard That Blighted My Life* with its comic chorus, so risqué to my innocent ears: *I'll raise a bunion on his Spanish onion if I catch him bending tonight. Olé!* Little did I know then that this sublime ditty was

Billy Merson

written and performed in character by Billy Merson: Nottingham's Own Comedian, born William Thompson in 1879, a few short years before my dear Nana, on Coalpit Lane, a cough and a spit away from her own natal inauguration. And it was many years later when I learned that our Billy had been all but bankrupted and nearly driven mental in pursuing ever-increasing costly cases through the law courts to receive royalties due as his intellectual property had been stolen by that vile burnt-corked caricature of a Negro Minstrel Al (and it disgusts me to spell out his benighted name) Jolson.

Conventional Wisdom—never to be trusted—has erroneously credited Jolson as the 'star' of 'the first talkie': *The Jazz Singer*. And it was in the follow-up to this success, accurately entitled *The Singing Fool*, that Jolson purloined Billy's purse. The truth is that Billy Merson had made talking pictures before the disgusting Jolson blacked up for the camera and the microphone. For Merson was an early pioneer of slapstick comedy films, none of which, unfortunately, survive. I like to think that his comedic ideas, if not their cinematic execution, might have been the equal of Buster Keaton. Perhaps that's wishful thinking. Yes, it certainly must be. Allow me my dreams. But some of Merson's early sound experiments do exist as well as wonderful recordings of the songs he wrote and performed when he was the talk of the town. His cheery autobiography, *Fixing The Stoof Oop*, came out in 1926 before his doomed-to-fail wrangles against lawyers representing the financial might of a powerful Hollywood studio. David's sling shots could never topple the mighty Warner Brothers Goliath. But his probably ghost-written words do recount the outrageous plots of his financially disastrous ventures in the screen trade which is all we have to go on. The brilliant career of this man who had once topped the bill at the Palladium went bung and he ended his life performing to dwindling audiences in out-of-town flea pits. This attempt to ventriloquise his voice is my tribute to a clown from our town. Suspension of Disbelief might be required to accept that Billy, in a state of mental anguish before his indigent demise, sought therapeutic counsel with a psychoanalytic disciple of the Viennese wizard. But what is credibility for if not to be stretched? The climactic hoary old chestnut from Lon Chaney's masterpiece *Laugh, Clown, Laugh* proved too tempting not to borrow… sorry, steal.

*

We find Billy as he finds his morning post.

> What? Not more bills! Tailor, Wine Merchant, Cobbler, Chemist…
> Oh no! Another brown envelope from my legal counsel:
> Mister Marchinup Q.C., Queer Cove!
> Suits, Booze, Boots, Boots, Marchinup… I'm down again.
> There's no discharge from the Law.
> (Do you like Kipling?
> Don't know, Billy, you naughty boy, I've never kippled.)

> Miss, take a missive, forthwith, with betht witheth. To Lincoln's Inn.
> Care of the Public Bar. (Don't mind if I do.) Lincoln's Inn. Gray's Out.
> And Chancery's Leg Before Wicket. Where was I? Ah, yes: Take a
> letter to my lawyer, from the residence of: William Henry Thompson
> Esquire. Better known as… (formerly known as?) Signor Billy Merson,
> O.B.E. Obsolete Blessèd Entertainer. *(Olé!)*

> Five years on the trot at the Royal Command Performance. And now
> thus reducèd.

> But they won't forget me, will they? Their Britannic Majesties…
> The Public!

> Remember me, Your Highnesses? It's Billy! Arch Rival and Forever
> Nemesis of: Alphonso Spagoni, the Toreador. *(Olé!)*
> (That's an 'ole with a haccent for the hignorant.)

> Always Top of the Bill for you, my people! Arise, Sir Billy, K.G.
> Knight of the Glory hole. Once a knight always a knight. Four shows
> a night and you're doing alright.

Night… After night… After night.

Where was I? Ah, yes: Take a lawyer to my letter:

Sir! Further to your ult. in respect of my inst. I await immediate apology for the disturbance you have caused my dear wife, Betty. She's a numble lass what hails from the sublime surrounds of Crocus Street, The Meadows. Ah! What a delectable address! Can these Nottingham nostrils e'er forget that romantic aroma? Tunney's Tannery, were it not? A sweet smell of a nasty stink. She's a ninnocent lass, bless her, ill-used to metropolitan ways. So when the poor old girl gasped: 'Dearest, there's someone at the door with a bill!' I was forced to explain that, since we now reside in a villa at Thames Ditton, we must anticipate the occasional visit from an itinerant mallard.

Where was I? Ah, yes: Sir! (Insufficiently emphatetic. Add two more plunks.)

Sir!!! Plunk, plunk, plunk!!! (That's more like it!) Having received your currant bun-cake… current invoice… for ruinous splendours… for services rendered… I would like to remind you: That I'm the one who is paid to make the jokes! (*Was* paid!)

If what you are offering is sound legal advice then I am a Dutchman!

Ja! Und I look forward to welcoming you to my windmill by the dyke there to dine upon the half-chewed tulip bulb upon which the missus and I have been subsisting since I paid your last bill, my duck! Plunk, plunk, plunk!!!

What exactly is your advice? Settle.

Settle. A forgotten town somewhere 'twixt Pontecraft and Carlisle. I played there… The Temperance Hall… the old Staircase Routine… when I was Snakella… Fixing me stoof oop. Settle! It was bad counsel then. Train fare and diggings cost more than my share of the takings.

If you call yourself a solicitor then I vow never to walk these streets again.

I am seriously considering transferring my legal business to Mister Onwud, of the law firm: Arfaleeg, Arfaleeg, Arfaleeg…

(Do I really have to? This is driving me to drink.)

Take a letter to the brewery: Ale have you know I'm mild and beer no bitter-ness, I'm lager than that, stout-hearted and never whine. Porter! On the double!

Do mind if I don't.

Maybe it was sound advice: 'Mister Thompson, accept what's on the table!'

Right-oh! Pass the salt!
'Listen to His Washup!'
Right-oh! Pass the tea-towel!

But I wasn't content with a pay-off, you see. I wanted my rightful due. What was lawfully mine. And what was I offered? Two thousand pounds!

Aye! Twa thoosand poond! Doesn't sound any bigger when I do a Harry Lauder!

Mind you, what more can you expect from a Judge with no fingers? Justice Thumbs. *(Olé!)*

Because it is, after all, my song. I remember so well when I wrote it. In panto. In Brighton, nineteen hundred and eight. My first year as a solo in that uplifting tale of Young Whit Dickington (as he's known in the trade), him as heard the midnight bells and became The Toast Of Old London Town. Not unlike my own story. And no, afore you ask, I was not, on that occasion, pulling off my justly-famed 'Dick'. I was cast as Idle Jack. Juvenile lead. With lovely Beatrice Allen (where is she now, we wonder?) in the role of Alice Fitzwarren, Alderman's daughter and Billy's inamorata.

'Twas first a duet in the Venetian style:

> *List to me, sweet senora*
> *While I sing you my love song tonight…*
> *(No, you won't!)*
> *Yes, I will!)*

Such a great hit. Such shrieks of mirth. I transformed it into a number for Billy alone:

> *List to me while I tell you*
> *Of the Spaniard that blighted my life (diddle-um)*

Gone all around the world, that song. And, in the course of its global perambulations, it has made many friends for me. (With one notable exception!) Because now… it's my bally jaw as is being dislocated! *(diddle-um)* by that… (Mother calling little Willy from Realms Above: No need to resort to language, dearest!) …by that… Spaniard!

Ah, my dear mother. If cleanliness really is next to godliness, then the holy angels bright must be coppering their wings up there in a happy land far, far away under my mam's persil jurisdiction. And I'll bet the old girl'll be even finding fault with the blessèd Saviour's stain removal capacity.

She never had it easy, mind, my old dear duck. Keeping filth at bay on Coalpit Lane.

Seven of us kids. Brothers: Joe, Ted, Harry, Fred and Steve with sister Nellie, sole soubrette. And, at the bottom of the bill: Little Willy! Nicknamed, by fellow classroom wits: 'Bowy!' On account of these poor pins of mine.
'Can't stop a pig in an entry!'
Well, what would any self-respecting porker be doing loitering up Coalpit Lane? Looking for company beneath his station? Or making a dash for freedom?

These membrances, ladies and gentlemen, haunt me no longer.
(As you can tell!)

For I swore from an early age that I would turn my disability to good account.

These bow legs would one day make my name and my fortune.
If they're going to chortle at my deformities then I was going to make them pay for it by God... manchester ((a town near Huntingdon, mam, honest. I played the Methodist Ladies Guild there. Fixing me stoof oop)

So I practised every night on the Forest. Sherwood Forest. Like some latter-day bow-leggèd Robin Hood. One day, I swore, I'd take their coin and leave them laughing, happy to be robbed by me.

The only thing I knew was that I was never going to end up like my poor hard-working father: 'Get an honest job, our Will.' The very name he'd baptised me with sounded like some coffinaceous testament. My poor dad... I would have willingly hung onto his every word, except he could never quite spit out a whole sentence on account of his hawking up of that dust from Coalpit Lane. You had to try and catch his drift... in mid-air usually... on the wing... all over the front of your shirt.

Still, the family never had to shell out for wallpaper paste given the contents of our dad's rattling chest. He grabbed hold of the lapel of me jacket, somewhat threadbare now after being handed-down by Joe, Ted, Harry, Fred and Steve, and he looked his youngest son in the eye: 'Is this...cough... what you really want to do, lad... cough, cough... play the goat?'

'I do, me dad. And I will, bedad! Else why did you name me 'Billy'?'

'Is this... hawk... a proper job...hawk, hawk... for a real man?'

I could hardly meet his gaze:

'You should have thought of that, our pa, before you sent me off to school in our Nellie's cast-off knickerbockers.'

I never saw the poor old sod… buster again.

I left this town as Will Thompson… to adopt my name on the bill as: Ping Pong Eccentric Equilibrilist! (still have trouble spitting it out!) Australia's Greatest Clown! (Don't ask! But it were four pound a week.)

> *Ah-diddle-ah-ah yodel ay-ee-de.*
> *Ah-diddle-ah-ah yodel ay-ee-de…*

Pardon me. You have to have a yodel of a morning after the mail has arrived. Alps you through the day. Them Switzers is peaceful folk, we must take a flake out of their snow balls. Mind you, their cuckoos look none too chuffed when the clock strikes midnight.

Where was I? Ah yes, my dear mother… The greatest regret of my life. She never lived to witness my fame. She never shared in the spoils. When I returned to my native town in glory, Nineteen Hundred and Eleven, I was a local legend. Hand me your bow, Robin of Loxley. I'm Top Of The Bill at the Empire: Nottingham's Own Comedian! I was Buttons. Little local lads jostled around just to scrape the paintwork off the motor and to drop lighted vestas in the Chauffeur's turn-ups.

A prophet honoured in his own home town at last. Nottingham's Own Comedian!

But me poor old duck was already bed-ridden. Too weak to make it to the best box reserved for her at the theatre. I did the next best thing and gave me mam the whole show at her bedside.

Buttons! A role any Swiss would roll over for! That perfect combination of Comedy and Pathos. Who among you is going to tell me that there's ever been a truer or more tragic part in all the history of drama Ancient and Modern? Shaw? Shaw-ly not! Cancel that Cheque-off! Euripides? Den I tear-a dose. Sophocles… I scoff, oh please! And Shakespeare?

Lezz un gemmun: Oner your-aw lift: That egg-breaking Prince of Denmark: Omlette. Ay-and oner you-aw roight: Cinderella's valet! Have you done up those flies, Buttons? We'll soon see whose melancholic antics makes their Highnesses the Public laugh… Or cry.

So I gave a Command Performance in Sneinton at her bedside for my mother, my own dear Queen. Such a shame she was already too far gone to laugh… Or cry.

But, I think even that sainted lady would understand and forgive my rage at that… (I won't profane, mam, promise) that… Jolson! (could there ever be a grosser malediction?) that… Al! (a syllable resorted to only in dire extremity.)

'Excuse me, my lady, I seem to have stepped in some Jolson what must have dripped out of your poodle's Al and now I've trod it all over your ladyship's Axminster.'

'Well, I'll be Jolson-ed. Al you!'

Al Jolson! I don't care what colour his face is. Real or assumed. It's the deep-dyed darkness of his soul that's bothering me. They say that he's Judaic-Al. As far as I'm concerned, he might just as well be Pentecost-Al. Why I despise this bulgar who blighted my life has nothing to do with his religion or his race… real or assumed. No, I hate the armhole because he's parasitic-Al. He's arf-inched my farquaring song without paying me a pith-helmeting penny.

My favourite song! How can I ever sing it again? My own song, which has now and forever become: 'Al Jolson's. *The Spaniard That Blighted My Life*. From his smash talking picture: *The Singing Fool.*' (I'm saying nowt!) But who's the fool now? For I'm turned down on appeal *(ding-dong-ding-dong)* by this Jolson-ing judge who's overthrown my cast-iron case on an Al-ing technicality. Not only do I lose the settlement (the measly two thou) but I'm also going to have to pay both sides' costs.

Fifteen Thousand Pounds! Aye. Fifteen thoosand poond! Afore we gang awa'! Far too much even for old Lauder even to contemplate. So says the Judge: 'Original copyright remains unviolated as a motion picture is a mechanical reproduction.'

Mechanical!
That, at least, is the one true word you spoke in the plaintiff Warner Brothers case, Your Honour! Justice Duff… From the law firm O'Feather, Wingsover…
(Do I have to?)

Motion pictures? Don't talk to me about films! I was an habituee of Celluloidia when Jolson was still crying for his mammy. I was making DeForest phonos when Al was still waiting for his Robert E. Lee.

Don't tell me you've already forgotten *Billy's Spanish Love Spasm*? I sold that one for a thousand pounds.
It was the other half dozen that all but beggared me.

What about *The Only Man*? Billy's madly in love with a shop girl who won't give him a second look. So, to cure him of his impossible infatuation, he's exiled to a happy land far, far away, where—stroke of genius I think you will agree—the only other inhabitants are Pretty Young Girls!

We shot that in Swansea. Billy was The Only Man surrounded entirely by Bunches of Beauty. I put an ad in the paper and four hundred of the local lovelies turned up to chase me 'cross the cliff tops. But, the real beauty was that every one of them worked for nowt. Just for the pleasure of being on screen with Bow-Leggèd Bill!

A fine crowd scene without spending a penny! (No, I refuse to stoop so low!)

My point being: Tell that to Buster Keaton!

You flocked to see it. Didn't you? Yet why didn't I make a brass farthing?

You see, we'd already agreed the sale price before the camera turned. But there was a war on and it wasn't all over by Christmas as promised. So costs started rising. Lighting, equipment, rentals, wood, canvas, paint… Everything shot up in price.

Not to mention labour. Any lad who might have been game enough to work for us was already out there in the trenches.

Don't look at me accusing! I was there the day war broke out. Offering myself for combat. The recruiting sergeant took one look at these appendages… And pocketed the king's shilling for himself. Bow-legs surplus to requirements in No Man's Land.

I did my bit for the war effort on the home front, raising morale with my two-reelers. We all had to make sacrifices. Talking of which… Forget about Pauline and her perils. Wat about my magnum opus *The Perils Of Pork Pie*? Nineteen Hundred and Fifteen. Billy eats a concoction of dubious content and then indulges in a weird nightmare which transports him back to Ancient Egypt in the age of the Pharoahs. Before its time, that picture was. If only we'd have released it after they unearthed King Tut's sarcophagus. But I have to ask myself: Was it worth it? You see, I used to love a pork pie—local speciality where I come from. But now, whenever I think about all the money that film never made I get Billy-ous. Can't bear to look a pork pie in the eye. There's a song in there somewhere. But I'm too pie-eyed to write it.

I'd give a million sighs for one of your pies, my Mummy!

*

Later. We discover Billy as he discovers himself.

I don't want to get all Greek over you, but, according to Aristotle (who kept an axolotl in a bottle) this might well be The Last Act. Hubristic theme: Had it all. Lost it all.

The motor: (Goodbye the Lagonda). The villa: (Chin Chin Thames Ditton). The missus: (Quack, quack, dearest Betty, my only duck). And nam poo the career. *(Olé!)*

All that's left: I'm reduced to a demeaning appearance half-way down the bill in 'The Golden Days Of The Old-Fashioned Music Hall'. Featuring... That Prehistoric Archaeological Exhibit, Billed-down Man. Coming soon (and leaving sooner) at a flea-pit near you.

Wi-Ki-Walla-Walla-Oo-Bah-Bay

Lost it all. I know, you don't have to tell me... A screw loose... a clause in my mental contract... I'm losing my sanity. (Do you believe in Sanity Claus?)

Take a letter to the asylum: Dear Sir or Madman...

So I was prevailed upon to go for a session... with the Hampstead Head Man. In matters of the mind I'm assured he's an expert. X is the unknown quantity and spurt is a drip under pressure.

If you can keep your head
When all around are losing theirs
Then you're a better mutt than I am,
Rin Tin Tin!

I've been in the wrong business. That head-shrinker cost more per minute than I ever pulled down when I was playing the Tivoli. Costs! A legal technicality. Fifteen thousand technicalities while we're getting technical.

This is killing me. Driving me to an early grave. Take a letter to the undertaker: Tomb It May Concern...

That alienist alienated me. He had no notion of what eminence could no longer spring up onto his couch. In the old days I would have walked out of his consulting room on my hands. Hark at the nerve of this nerve-wallah:
'Last night I visited a proletarian Palace of Varieties at the unfashionable end of the Finchley Road...'
Frognall? Or do you always walk like that?
(Oh, do I really have to? It doesn't even make sense any longer.)
'Purely in the interests of science, you understand. I'm preparing a

monograph on: *The Compulsion to Joke: Gags and their relation to Eroto-maniacal Psycho-sexual-pathology.*' Plunk! Plunk! Plunk-ety Plunk!

Thank God… Al…ming (a market town in Surrey where I once entertained the worshipful members of the Masonic Lodge, honest) my poor mother's not around to overhear this filth—there wouldn't be sufficient soap in the heavenly realms to wash out his oral phase!

'A clapped-out old has-been came on stage in a bald ginger wig, a moth-eaten frock coat and ill-fitting trousers. A true throw-back to the primitive tastes of a less sophisticated age. And he performed a routine which voiced barely disguised sentiments of hatred and revenge against the Father, sublimated, condensed and displaced onto a figure of nothing less than a Bullfighter! I surely don't have to spell out the evident phallic symbolism, do I, Mister Thompson?'

And then the penny dropped. Vacant became Engaged. The bulgar must be talking about my song! All I can say is that I hope he never comes into contact with *On the Good Ship Yacki Hicki Doola.* Who knows what he'd make of those naval shenanigans!

The expert spurts: 'It confirms my intuition that popular trifles…'
(More sherry, vicar?)

'…allow far greater access into the operation of the collective unconscious…'
(Allow me to take the collection)

'…than the works of any modern writer, as for instance: Yeats…'
(And I bet you ignorant lot don't have a clue as to the function of a yate!)

'…or even by a timeless poetic genius, such as Shakespeare himself.'

You…Spaniard! It took me three months to get that song right! Have you never considered that the Bard was a four-times-a-night trouper just like Snakella or Ping-Pong? What about the night I appeared as Macbeth:

> *I acted so tragic the house rose like magic*
> *The audience cried: 'You're sublime!'*
> *They made me a present of Mornington Crescent*
> *And threw it a brick at a time.*

In three hundred years the egg-heads will be analysing my odes:

> *If I can't get my Desdemonia*
> *I won't hang around to catch pneumonia*
> *I'm going to put my trousers on*
> *I'm going back to Wigan*
> *Where the tripe comes from.*

(Mind you, that might not make much sense… unless they've seen me do it in the shortie toga, plucking the lyre… and I suppose that piece of celluloid will have long since been melted down for its silver content.)

This fungus-faced anal-ist pursued his point from the comfort of his armchair… with your poor old Billy flat out on the couch:
'There was even a line… I made a note of it somewhere… Ah, yes:
And as I went out for some __nuts__ and a programme the __dirty dog__ stole her away!

'What else can we assume? Is this not a hidden confirmation, coded unconsciously in an erstwhile popular song, of the primacy and universality of the Oedipal urge?'

How double dare he! My innocent words! Twisted and, with a winking of the eye, a nudging of the elbow, and much indication towards those parts of the body never to be washed except infrequently and from behind a curtain and then only to be dried with a really scratchy towel. Words now endowed with filthy imbrications. Dirty meanings never intended by someone who penned those words in the first place. Someone who was, after all: Me!

What was this bonce wallah intimating? Was he really suggesting that deep inside my secret heart I want to Al my dad up the swannee and Jolson my dear old mammy?

The Spaniard That Blighted My Life is a jolly ditty about a chap vowing to get his own back on someone who stole away his special girl, who just happens, in this particular, the location being Spain, to be an antagonist, not unnaturally, of the masculine variety of the bovine species! To whit: A Fighter of Bulls!

If I catch Alphonso Spagoni, the toreador
With one mighty swipe I will dislocate his bally jaw
I'll find this bullfighter, I will
And when I catch the bounder the blighter I'll kill
He shall die, he shall die
He shall die tiddly i-ti-ti-ti-ti-ti-ti!

There's no hidden meaning in this song:

I'll raise a bunion
On his spanish onion
If I catch him bending tonight. Olé!

What could be more straightforward than that!

But this trick-cyclist was still psych-aling away: 'I must confess that he would perhaps have once been a most amusing fellow. I counsel you that a certain cure for your depression would be to go and see this superannuated comic. One thing you'll realise, Mister Thompson, is that there's always someone far madder than you are. Go and see him, before it's too late. Give yourself a laugh. Go and see this Billy Merson.'

I AM BILLY MERSON!

TIME AND SILENCE—ELIOT STANNARD.

I confess I only became acquainted in 1999 with the work of Eliot Stannard, whom I now dub 'The Patron Saint of British Screenwriters', when I read the ground-breaking book *English Hitchcock* by my friend Charles Barr. He made the ungainsayable argument that many of Stannard's innovations in cinematic story-telling anticipated the work of far better known film-makers who continue to be lauded in the pantheon of film history. Suitably inspired and fired up, I subsequently attempted to track down Stannard's articles in the cracking and yellowing pages of the cinematic trade journals of the silent film era in which this 'scenarist' outlined with supreme confidence, not devoid perhaps of justifiable narcissism, his principles of what would now be

Eliot Stannard

termed 'screenwriting.' Stannard had every right to be so proudly outspoken because he was, as far as I know, the only toiler in the trade in this country to distil a theory from a recently begotten craft and to share with his readers practical and creative insights derived from a lifetime of experience. In an age when bookshop shelves groan under the weight of bogus manuals with titles such as 'How To Write Screenplays That Sell And Will Make You A Fortune', I found these early reflections on the tools of our trade truly revelatory and still applicable to practitioners today.

Like many great artists before they find their unique 'voice', the young Hitch, who began his artistic career in the film studios as a fine illustrator of inter-titles but who aspired to so much more, has been accurately characterised as a 'sponge', soaking up every possible influence around him. When he had sucked Stannard dry he tossed him aside, increasingly relying on the every bit as acute writerly structural knowledge of his lifelong companion, Alma Reville (Nottingham born, lest we forget). At least, that's how it may well have seemed to Stannard, whose high-born bohemian nose must have put been truly out of joint by these suburban interlopers—even more so when the talkies came in and he was considered a dinosaur, a relic of the past, like so many other erstwhile professionals.

Wishing to champion a belated recognition of this now forgotten man I wrote a feature for *Sight and Sound* in 2005, but I wanted to take it further. In his book Charles Barr suggested that Eliot Stannard's relationship with the fledgling Alfred Hitchcock would make a great drama: the would-be Director standing in for Prince Hal with the skilled Writer playing his Falstaff—though the respective girth of the two principals would presumably have to be reversed in this instance. I willingly took up the torch and pitched this story as a radio play—with a disappointing lack of response which Stannard would have understood only too well. I therefore came up with this monologue which I first performed at the wonderful British Silent Film Festival, curated biannually by Laraine Porter and Bryony Dixon. The original article is appended because, though there is a certain overlap, it includes some quotations from the horse's mouth and provides an historical perspective to the rancorous recriminations of my made-up man.

*

The London office of the Motor Vehicle Licensing Department during the Blitz.

A chain-smoking wheezing geezer does his utmost not to file a pile of forms.

I am Eliot Stannard.

Very well… I didn't exactly expect the rafters to be raised.
What's in a name?

I am more than resigned to the irony that nominal recognition accounts for little in what is (what *was*) my chosen vocation. Indeed, the very fact that none of you acknowledge me at all is enough to prove the point.: In this business Anonymity Is True Celebrity.

But I *am* Eliot Stannard.

Very well, then, bugger you! Do you really not know who I am? I who wrote the rule book of pictorial tale-telling? I am a… no, too late for false modesty… I am the Pioneer Kinematographic Scenarist!

And even that eludes you? You all think I just write those sub-titles, don't you?

'Meanwhile… In Lady Effingham's Boudoir… Dot… Dot… Dot…'

Oh… What's in a trade? Very well, then, let's start again.

I *was* Eliot Stannard.

Now I'm Mister John Strange Winter, a shabby-genteel, down-at-heel clerk.

Will that do for characterisation? And what about the properties?

This De Retski Minor… ('the ten-minute smoke for intelligent folk') was once a Romeo y Julieta. This bottle of Doctor Collis Browne's

84

patent bronchial decongestant... ('guaranteed oblivion for one and a tanner') was once a chilled flute of the sparkling Widow. This copy of 'Picturegoer'... was once 'The Kinematograph and Lantern Weekly', in which, I, yes, I had a regular by-line, billed as: 'The Master of Screen Technique'. This dreary pile of driving license application forms... was once a stack of shooting scripts. And this drab Motor Vehicle Licensing Department... was once the glorious studio of Gainsborough Pictures.

And now what do I read? That Fat Owl—who purloined and bowdlerised from yours truly without a scintilla of gratitude or recognition, everything for which he now takes credit... And who, when we were first introduced, could certainly fill a suit, but knew damn all about how to fill a screen. This Obese Oaf is: 'Shooting A Picture' for David O. Selznick (the 'O' stands for 'Nothing'). Starring: Ingrid ('Would You Mind Saying That Again In English?') Bergman, in Hooray for SodomAndGomorrahWood.

What's it called, eh: 'Spellbound.' 'Smell-Pound' more like. Surrealism, is it now, Hitch? Gallic Gallimaufry! Of course, it was all Expressionism in those days.

I told him... what did I tell him about Dream Sequences: 'Leave that guff to the Hun, Fatso!' He had the nerve to retort, damn him: 'Cinema might one day become the actualisation of The Psychopathology Of Everyday Life'.

I called his bluff: 'And I predict that Kinematography will forever be the pictorial expression of Common Sense.'

What a prophet!

He always was attracted to grotesquely indecent and un-English scenes of gilded vice which pander to lewd minds and carnal appetites like his own. ('Call me Hitch and never mention the Cock')

No wonder our cousins across the Herring Pond have taken his fat form to their debased bosoms. The whole bloody world is being taught to think in 'American-ese'. They'll even take credit for winning our war.

A Story must proceed through obstacles. That's the essence of Drama. According to Aristotle... But I'm getting ahead of myself. I used to maintain that in Film, as in Life, we are faced with two great obstacles: Time and Silence.

Well, I was right, I suppose. Small Time now remains before the Long Silence.

I could tell you my story… But I don't believe in Flashbacks:
a decadent trope entirely antithetical to good British notions of
forward Imperial progress. Nevertheless, seeing as it was myself who
effortlessly condensed the life of Admiral Nelson into ninety minutes
of screen time…

DISSOLVE. (Last refuge of a cinematographic scoundrel. However,
needs must)

The screen goes runny like a stinking, over-ripe cheese (doubtless French).
TITLE: *Thirty Years Before.* (Before that war which was supposed to end
to all wars. That war which took so many of our dearest chums away.)

Stifle sentiment! Get to The Rules!

RULE ONE: Symbolism.

The essence of scenographic story-telling distillation lies in the subtle
and unemphatic deployment of images which take on a greater
meaning when juxtaposed with other images. For example:

> *High… High in a tree… On a far-flung branch… A nest… Where baby
> birds jostle for open-mouthed attention as the Mother returns with food for her
> brood. Maternally, she proffers worms into their gaping maws. Only one mouth
> remains unfed, unsatisfied… that of the youngest, the favourite, her pet. His
> poor beak gapes open, begging, unsatisfied…*

D'you not see? This is precisely the technique I, and I alone, invented
for that picture: *Justice.* Oh, don't tell me you haven't seen it?
Why do I remain unastounded? Those pinch-penny scapegraces…
(Footnote One: The pertinent deployment of an apposite adjective
will always help to nail down characterisation and curtail actorly
interpretation) …those studio panjandrums, who enriched themselves
from my hard labour, probably melted down the only extant copy to
retrieve the dregs of silver from the negative.

Definition of the Cinema: a place of apparent entertainment where
only Fleas and Producers go out with what they came in for.
A sanctioned site where blood suckers thrive.

Justice!

Allow me to appraise you of my own innovative experimentation. To
hammer home the pain of a man in prison I needed you to feel the
horror of solitary confinement. It was I, the Scenarist, not that witless,
credit-seeking Producer, who came up with the idea of:

A Human Being behind bars…

CUT TO: *A Wild Bird at liberty soaring ever upwards into the sky…*

It was I, the Dramatist, not Maurice Elvey (L.V. stands for 'Lacks Vision') who wrote:

CUT BACK TO: *He paces his cell...*

And then, so that you might understand the felon is crippled with guilt, I display this jail-bird's dark mental agony by contrast with:

CUT TO: *Innocent Children playing in bright sunshine...*

It was I, the Scenario Writer, not that feted West End gab-merchant Galsworthy who wrote 'The Original Play' set in three rooms, it was I, Stannard, whose name now no-one knows, who scripted these words:

CUT BACK TO: *The Condemned Man's eyes look down at his criminal hands...*

Now, you see, this picture means nothing by itself. It's simply a photograph of what every one of us has in the middle of the face and at the end of the arms. But, so that you, yes you, every member of the audience, might feel what he feels, must know what it is like to possess the foul fingers of a transgressor:

CUT IN WITH: *The toiling hands of an Honest Labouring Man working in his garden, stained only by the dirt of the wholesome soil. As the evening sun sinks...*

Another symbolic conflict: Between the freedom of honest toil and the enforced indolence of captivity!

DISSOLVE TO: *The Shadow Of The Scaffold!*

What could be more bold, more telling? Without the use of a single word.

These days it seems the Film Clique label Symbolism, my greatest inspiration, 'Intellectual Montage'. 'Montage', I'm informed, is the French word for 'sodomy'. And as for 'Intellectual' ... The high-brow know-nothings claim it as an invention of the Bolsheviks. Our allies now.

Strange Times breed Strange Bedfellows. I sleep alone. But who can rely upon a good night's sleep in these times?

What was I saying? Ah yes, Symbolism. The more we make use of it the better our film will be.

Where were we? Ah yes, back to the nest.

The mother bird then pierces her own breast and the runt of the litter drinks deep from her sacrificial bosom. Only she knows how much she loves him. Only she knows that she must lose him... Only the mother can understand that her fledgling must find his own wings... And fly!

But Poetic Imagery must always be rooted in Everyday Reality. Resist the temptation to be too flighty lest your wings might be clipped or you may soar too close to the sun.

RULE TWO: Atmosphere!

We stand (Footnote Two: Who is this 'We'? It is 'I' who dictates. It is 'You' who must witness) I stand (I stood) on the shoulders of the Old Masters in the creation of mood and sentiment through light and shade.

TILT DOWN TO: *From the tree… To a Mayfair doorway… On the threshold of which stands an immaculately dressed Young Man adjusting the carnation in his buttonhole. As…* (Footnote Three: 'As'… Implying simultaneity of action. 'As', that simple two-letter friend of every Scenarist), should this be shown with a CUT? Or a DISSOLVE? Why not let 'we' allow the Producer to earn his inflated salary for once by having to cope with this little conjunction?

As the handsome young fellow kisses the tear-stained cheek of his doting Mother who stands, proud yet broken-hearted… (Footnote Four: Two contradictory emotions at the same time! Actors Are Livestock. Hired by the yard. Why not set *them* a problem to justify their narcissism? When did Scenarists ever have a 'Green Room'?)

TITLE*: Our Hero: Young* ELIOT STANNARD.

And down the Mayfair street he walks (too prosaic?) *strides…* (too athletic?) *marches…* (too military?) *strolls…* (too nonchalant?) *glides…* (uhm, very possible.)

Bugger it.

RULE THREE: Continuity.

Kinematography tells stories by means of deeds—let the plot be replete with Action. Dispense with redundancy. Keep the story flowing.

CUT TO: INT. STUDIO. DAY. The Studio. Where once I was King in all but title. Where I first met that obese oik: The Name Above the Title. (Would someone mind telling me: Where exactly is Leytonstone? It's off the map of that metropolis with which I am familiar. An unfashionable suburb way out East, far, far from the well-appointed streets and leafy squares of Mayfair).

For I have, at last count: One Hundred and Sixteen Titles to my name. Eighty-seven screenplay credits already before he ever came on the scene. An entry in the Collis Browne Book of Records. A plaque in the De Retski Minor Hall of Fame. From: *'The Sound Of Her Voice'*

(Nineteen Fourteen.) To: *'Brighton With Gladys'* (Nineteen Thirty-Three.) That was the last count. There will be no more.

Stick to the point! Oh, what *is* the point?

RULE FOUR: Theme.

The most important rule of all. This is *really* Rule One.

For now at last we have our CAST. Not a preening parade of over-paid performers. But the Four Pillars of Kinematographic Wisdom. An alchemical formula to transform debased West End theatrical lead and lending-library novelistic dross into Pure Cinematic Gold.

Continuity, Atmosphere, Symbolism and, above all: Theme. CAST.

A successful film-play depends upon the soundness of its Central Theme, and that theme must never be lost sight of by the Scenario-writer. Every Scene which does not bear upon the central theme is just an Incident... a blemish to the Scenario. And must be ruthlessly excised... even should it be a darling Scene which you have loved.

A Great Unifying Theme.

Not a series of improbable situations chasing each other in bewildering rapidity like an urchin running a stick across a line of park railings. No... a skeletal motif upon which the body of every story must be constructed—even my own story.

What, then, should be the theme of: *Stannard—A Life?*

Decline, Disillusion... A noble tragedy!

Dismissal and Despair... A pathetic melodrama!

Hardly Redemptive.

Nothing has disturbed my plot for over a decade. Such is my quotidian existence:

A Motor Vehicle License application arrives on my desk. I file it alphabetically.

But... Symbolically:

TITLE: *The wheel turns. The ever-revolving wheel. That relentless, remorseless Wheel of Fate.* (D. W. Griffith be damned. Another one of my cinematic inventions!)

This terrible need for perpetual motion is displayed by a photograph of:

A chariot wheel... (Greek? Did they have chariots? Roman? Would look like any old wheel. Assyrian? Ah, yes... primordial!) *With a protruding scythe cutting down everything that lies in its path. Chopping Promise. Severing*

Possibility. With a Knife… Blah-blah-blah *Knife*… Mumble-mumble-mumble *Knife*.

Blackmail. That's when it all went skew-whiff. When they started to babble.

That's when he abandoned me. He took what he needed and squeezed me dry. It's me who should blackmail that cockney spawn of a greengrocer for purloining my innovations. Oh, Gor blimey *Knife*.

What did I predict?

Speaking pictures would destroy the true illusion of Kinema and lengthen scenes beyond endurance.

What did I predict?

That the talkies were a nine-days wonder and never last.

What did I predict?

That the uniquely international language of pictorial tale-telling would never be supplanted by words.

What a prophet!

Well, I was right at least in the case of *To Brighton With Gladys*—one of my few gabbling efforts. It was originally entitled *To Brighton With A Bird*—for you see Gladys was a penguin, liberated from London Zoo! But our protector the censor banjaxed that.

Ah, it always was a cut-and-slash trade. Then why am I unable to shut up about it?

Get back to the Theme. The Central Theme. What is the Theme of this little life?

How are the mighty fallen. Tell it not in Gainsborough. Publish it not in 'The Kinematograph and Lantern Weekly'. Lest the daughter of the Revilles rejoices. And that corpulent, uncircumcised bastard triumphs.

Remember Aristotle: Every drama must have a Beginning, a Middle and an End.

I beg you 'Arry, old chap: Must it always be that relentless order?

The Bright Beginning. The Muddling Middle. The Inevitable Closing Title:

THE END. The Bitter End. *Finis*.

Maybe one day I, Eliot Stannard will be remembered. I predict that in another, more enlightened time, devoted cognoscenti will meet in darkened rooms to share the long-forgotten truth that it was I who raised the British film to the apotheosis of Dramatic Art.

90

And now… Parnassus beckons… A place for me if only on a lower slope. But in eternity will Mister Alfred Double-Gutted Two-Dinners Spatchcock be flapping his adipose wings up there in the firmament far above me in the Seventh Heaven of the Seventh Art?

Time and Silence. No more Time. Time for Silence… Silents.

*

THE PATRON SAINT OF BRITISH SCREENWRITERS.

'Our two greatest difficulties: Time and Silence.' – Eliot Stannard.

Today's viewers, largely unaccustomed to the artistry of silent films (especially those which emanated from these isles) might well scratch their heads when faced with a question posed in 1920: 'What is a Scenario Writer?' But it seems likely that readers of one of the earliest screenwriting manuals were equally nonplussed at the time of its publication, eight years or so before the widespread introduction of sound. For the author ruefully admits: '(S)ome of the Public believe this mystical and almost mythical person merely writes those fragments of explanation or dialogue technically known as sub-titles.' (And now usually referred to as 'inter-titles').

On those unavoidable occasions when the embarrassed screenwriter is forced to reveal his, in the present instance, trade (and once the inevitable confusion about 'sign-writing' has been cleared up) it is remarkable how frequently 'the Public' still assume that our job is merely to contribute the dialogue—those, that is, already sophisticated enough to know that the words are not made up by the actors. Little seems to have changed since the appearance of 'Writing Screen Plays' by Eliot Stannard.

Who is Eliot Stannard? If the name is recognised these days it would most likely be for his writing credits on eight of Alfred Hitchcock's silent films— from his directorial debut (*The Pleasure Garden* in 1925) to his penultimate silent picture (*The Manxman* in 1929) and including such highly-regarded pictures as *The Lodger* and *Downhill*. If there has been any recent rehabilitation of Stannard's contribution it would be entirely due to Charles Barr's dogged detective work undertaken for his essential book 'English Hitchcock'.

Stannard, however, had already garnered over eighty screenwriting credits since he started in the trade in 1914, a decade before the artistically-gifted grocer's son from Leytonstone waddled into Gainsborough Studios as a designer of titles. Equally significantly, Stannard was one of the very first practitioners of the profession who thought seriously and wrote publicly about exactly what it takes to be a writer for the screen. His articles about the craft remain, to my mind, perhaps more analytical and definitely far more useful than the shelves full of 'How To' volumes which have proliferated in recent years. These publications must be produced for the most part by disaffected scribes who have come to the realisation that it's far less mentally challenging and much less ego-shattering to churn out a self-help manual than to keep on having to pitch up in the bloody arena. I can't say I'm unsympathetic but that does not mean I have to read them.

Give me Eliot Stannard any day. He was a successful scenarist who, through trial and error and supreme confidence in his own abilities, helped write the rule book. His work is still worth engaging with even if, perhaps especially because, he was writing before the sound barrier was broken.

Stannard's first principles: The scenario writer must be 'thoroughly experienced in each technical branch of Kinematography; possessed of dramatic training and a sense of Theatre; conversant with the laws of literary construction; a student of psychology and character; and alive to the atmospheric value of costume, furniture, architecture and scenery'. How many of today's 'script editors' (whose companies have stumped up for them to attend a weekend seminar by some screenplay guru) could honestly admit themselves adept at even one of these five essential requisites? Mind you, how many writers could?

Above all, Stannard, more than any of his native contemporaries, recognised the paramount importance of what he called 'construction', what we would call 'narrative structure'. By far the majority of the scenarios he worked on were not truly original stories but adaptations of novels, plays, historical or biographical subjects, sometimes poems and even on one occasion a much-reproduced painting: *The Laughing Cavalier* no less! This state remains much the same, for it is a reckless producer who is prepared to gamble upon a 'property' which is not somehow 'pre-sold'.

Stannard's break came through adapting a tale written by his own mother, an immensely popular and equally prolific novelist who gloried in the *nom-de-plume* of John Strange Winter. In the course of his career he adapted the works of such eminent literary figures as Fielding, Dickens, Emily Bronte and Shakespeare as well as currently popular playwrights such as Galsworthy, Coward and Novello into cinema. But whatever the source material he was dealing with, high or low, Eliot Stannard soon learned that the process of transformation into an effective scenario should never be the preserve of 'the lowest form of literary hack... a cut-and-slash trade'. Cinema, he argued, is a specific medium and it must develop its own particular methods of communicating stories and emotions.

In the first of a series of articles on 'The Art of Kinematography', published in *The Kinematograph and Lantern Weekly* in May 1918, he shared his secrets for the construction of screen dramas. His founding principles might be glossed mnemonically as CAST—not those fêted denizens of the green room whose names the ignorant Public knew only too well—but Continuity, Atmosphere, Symbolism and Theme.

Unlike the writer of plays—who can develop the psychology of the characters through the spoken word—or the writer of prose fiction—who 'can expiate to any length on the thoughts that are passing through the minds of his characters'—the kinematographic narrative has to tell stories through continuous action. About his 1918 version of the popular play *Hindle Wakes* (the first of two directed by Stannard's frequent collaborator at this time, Maurice Elvey) he writes: '(I)n Stanley Houghton's play... we are only *told* of Fanny's adventure in Blackpool with her employer's son, but in the film version we *see* every detail of that riotous adventure.'

Continuity, though, does not simply allow us access to sights beyond the confines of the proscenium arch. It can radically transform the relationship between the viewer and the tale through the choreography of knowledge.

Lady Audley's Secret, Mary Elizabeth Braddon's sensational best-seller of 1862 was a stalwart of the stage and had twice been made into a film before the version that Stannard churned out in 1920. The book, like many a mystery story, starts *in media res* and only well into the tale are readers treated to melodramatic revelations of the mysterious lady's past nefarious actions.

The film script, however, lays out the incidents of the plot chronologically... in continuity. Viewers see how the low-born woman (memorably played by Margaret Bannerman) attempts murder to secure her elevated social position. We spectators, therefore, know far more about her than the other characters in the drama. The questions of the Reader: 'Who is this woman and what is the secret of her past?'. The questions of the Spectator: 'What more must she do to cover up her crime and will she get away with it?'

Stannard never wrote himself about his fine cinematic version but it's clear that this 'straight-line adaptation', taking his viewers from the outset into the clandestine life of the central character, was a choice prompted by psychology, furthering his credo that we are not simply interested in what characters do but in understanding their 'motive(s) for doing so.' Today we cannot but be struck that this method of continuity construction results in a pattern of Suspense which would normally be deemed 'Hitchcockian'... rather than 'Stannardian'.

'Atmosphere' should also be an expression of character and is therefore part of the writer's remit, too important to be left in the hands of the Art Department. The writer has to know the minutest of details about the biography of the *dramatis personae* even if most of these peccadilloes will never find their way onto the screen. Appreciative as he was of the contribution of what he called 'the unseen' (lab workers, scene shifters, cutters, projectionists, cinema musicians who form the other ranks of this glamorous industrial army) it is the job of the writer to know what rooms the characters inhabit, what possessions they own, what clothes they wear. An obvious enough insight, perhaps. But how often, both on stage and screen, do we suspect that designers might be producing their visions to elicit admiring gasps from their fellow designers?

When it comes to 'Symbolism' the contribution of our forgotten man to the language of cinema is truly surprising. Denied dialogue, instances of, say, power and dominance must be conveyed symbolically through staging, lighting, cutting. This might seem just a common-sensical matter of *mise-en-scène*, though it remains a sore point for the poor writer who all too often has to sacrifice control only to face critical calumny when the director shoots the text rather than the sub-text.

Don't start me off... Back to Uncle Eliot. When Stannard writes of his adaptation of John Galsworthy's *Justice* (about the devastating effects of an inhumane penal system upon a young bank clerk, Falder, who committed a trivial crime for altruistically mitigating motives) it is amazingly evident that Stannard's notion of 'symbolism' encompasses a far more original aspiration for cinema semantics. It's worth quoting at some length for there's no other way to assess how well this experiment worked because the film (another Elvey production released in 1917) is lost.

> *In his great play... Galsworthy relies upon the intonation of the actor's voice for much of his pathos and even his meaning. To translate these conditions and obtain the same effect through so different a medium as kinematography... I resorted to symbolism. To show the horrors of solitary confinement I showed in rapid succession: Falder locked in his cell; a dog chained to his kennel; a small bird imprisoned in a tiny cage; then in equally quick succession: happy children free from care romping in a sun-lit garden; a dog racing happily after a tennis ball; a lark soaring up to the heavens.*

In the play the Defence Counsel orates: 'Justice is a machine that... rolls on of itself.' In the picture this is made manifest by, as a triumphant review of the Stannard/Elvey picture put it: 'an Assyrian chariot wheel, with the protruding scythe that cuts down without pity everything in its path.' What else is this but an instance of Eisenstein-ian 'intellectual montage'? But *Justice* was produced in England in 1917, the very year of the Bolshevik Revolution not, like *October*, for the tenth anniversary. And who was it imagined this graphic impression of 'the extraordinary contrast between captivity and liberty'? The original playwright? The director? Come off it! It was the humble scenarist, ever the lowliest figure on the cinematic totem pole, bearing the weight of grander icons pressing down upon the shoulders.

It's when he insists upon the organising centrality of 'Theme' that Stannard bellows beyond the years into the ever unreceptive ears of today's toilers in the vineyard. For him, the 'universal error' of bad scripts is that they are: 'composed of a series of exciting incidents and nothing else... improbable and often impossible situations follow each other in bewildering rapidity... every scene which does not bear directly upon the central theme is a blemish to the scenario.'

One thing Stannard was certain of was that the introduction of sound would be: 'a ghastly failure'. What a prophet! For his was one of many careers that never survived the transition to talkies despite his assurance: 'It is a dangerous and hazardous pastime to gaze into the future... (But) one prophecy which is sure of fulfilment is that nothing will ever persuade Eliot Stannard to disappear from the kinematograph industry.'

But disappear he most certainly did. The theme of his life story: How are the mighty fallen! Time's scythe has wrought its work of Silence upon our ancestor of whom Michael Powell, himself so long in the English wilderness, said he 'could talk like an angel and forever'. Patrick McGilligan, in his biography of Hitchcock, has Stannard working in some minor capacity for Gaumont in 1944, the year of his death, doubtless pathetically raging against the treacheries of the now-lauded Hollywood *auteur* who stole from him all he knew and decamped to the tents of the ungodly in Hollywood.

But Charles Barr tells another story gleaned from fellow writer Sidney Gilliat's unpublished memoirs. In this alternative version Stannard finds himself working as a lowly clerk in a Motor Vehicle Licensing Department. Brooding over the cruel exigencies of Fate in the boozer after work, he decides to return to the office—objective correlative of the enormity of his reduction in status—where he systematically rearranges the hated files 'with a view to causing the maximum disturbance for the longest possible time.' Then the Trickster walks out amidst the exploding doodlebugs, never to be seen again. I know which ending Stannard the Writer would have preferred for his biopic.

There's no Blue Plaque, no biography. Most of the one hundred and sixteen(!) films for which he has a credit are missing believed dead. Marginal, ephemeral, unappreciated, obliterated, now is the hour for Eliot Stannard to be honoured as The Patron Saint of British Screenwriters.

THE ARCHITECT RETURNS—ROBERT TAYLOR.

Bromley House has been a private Subscription Library since the 1820s, appreciated by the members yet unknown to most of the folk who pass its all-but-hidden doorway, on Angel Row in Nottingham. They have scant awareness that, behind the facades of the charity shop and burger bar which now surround the entrance, is a beautifully laid-out walled garden, a haven in the heart of the city centre. The house itself was built in 1752 and attempts at urban renovation (for which read despoliation) have been successfully resisted. A member myself, I was approached by Julia Wilson, the then Librarian,

Sir Robert Taylor

to participate in a fund-raising programme to commemorate the two hundred and fiftieth anniversary of the building. I came up with this site-specific promenade performance which would take the audience through some of the rooms in the building's four storeys.

There is a contention—though backed up, it must be said, by little documentation—that this well-appointed town house from the middle of the eighteenth century had been designed by Sir Robert Taylor, the pre-eminent Palladian-influenced architect of the British baroque. My conceit was to bring back Taylor from the grave for him to decide whether his post-mortem memories might settle the argument. Taylor did, after all, take commissions from banks, and Bromley House was originally the commercial premises of a Nottingham banker, George Smith, whose Banking Hall would have been on the first floor with the domestic apartments on the storeys above. The more research I did, however, the less I was convinced that Taylor might have been the architect of Bromley House. If so this would have been, I think, the northernmost of his endeavours as most of his work was in London and the Home Counties. Such a verdict would not, of course, have suited my purpose so I determined to accentuate the positive. There are some architectural historians who are convinced this is, indeed, a 'genuine Taylor' while others dismiss this, presumably, as provincial wishful thinking—the only book-length study by Marcus Binney (*Sir Robert Taylor—From Rococo to Neo-Classicism*, 1984) never mentions Bromley House, George Smith or Nottingham. Fortunately, the role of the dramatist is not to pretend to be an amateur architectural historian, but to imagine the character of the Architect who returns.

(Photographs of the interior, exterior and the garden of Bromley House can be found at www.visitnottinghamshire.co.uk, search 'Bromley House Library'.)

*

He bursts into the room:

Ladies and Gentlemen… (Not that, looking around, you seem to be especially distinguished representatives of either of those categories that I might once have recognised.) I wish I could say with any degree of candour that it gives me pleasure to be back here. There I was… Perfectly contented… Up on Parnassus… Quaffing nectar with my architectural mentor:

> *Andrea Palladio, he was quite a lad, you know!*
> *When they said: 'Your work's baloney!'*
> *He designed Palazzo Ragione,*
> *When accused: 'You're out for Glory!'*
> *He came up with San Giorgio Maggiore.*

Matter of fact, when my name momentarily eluded him, I engaged him with a *bon mot* directed against that *other* English 'builder': 'Madam, I'm *not* Adam!!!'

Why am I unamazed to see you're not smiling? Neither did the great Italian, as it happened. Until I explained: It's a Palladian-drome!

Oh, what fun it is to be dead! And then I find myself summoned back down here. To Nottingham of all benighted spots. Only for an afternoon, I was assured.

Angel Row! Thought this was supposed to be a day off! I found only fallen angels in Yates's Wine Lodge. Didn't recognise this place at first. Did I really design this residence? I have a vague memory that it was built for a financier. A man with a considerable amount of expendable wealth. What *was* his name? I always made it a point to seek out bankers for my clients. Far more reliable than the landed gentry when it came to invoicing. What was the man called? Yes…It was Smith! George Smith. An honest, self-forged name, entirely devoid of pretension. Not unlike mine own. Taylor! Robert Taylor! *Sir* Robert Taylor!

So why is it *Bromley* House? Nowhere near the London borough. And is this really one of my works? Does anyone in these times

manifest the slightest interest in or appreciation of my works? One
slender academic monograph and a monochromatic spread in:
'Country Life'.

(As an avowed urbanite I have to wonder: contradiction in terms,
or what?)

Scant appreciation for a lifetime's dedication to Form and Proportion.
Sic transit gloria mundi... (And Tuesday, Wednesday and every other
blessèd day of the week, 'twould appear.)

Not that it was always thus: 'His works entitle him to a distinguished
rank in the first class of British Architects.' That's what is proclaimed
upon my memorial. In the Abbey, of course!

Oh yes, don't ever imagine that *amour propre* expires with this vile body.
We're very mindful of reputation, you know... Up there. Immortality
is the object of the exercise after all. Old Wren has become almost
unapproachable. Head even bigger than that ridiculous edifice of his.

> *Christopher Wren said to some men:*
> *'Don't expect me 'at home' I'm erecting a dome.'*

And you should see Mad Nick...

> *Hawksmoor talks more*
> *Than any other feller*
> *Since he starred in a best-seller.*

Praise still puffs up. Brickbats bruise. And what about neglect?
So, with your connivance, I shall tell them all, back up there, that this
has been the private rehearsed reading of my one-man show,
presented before a select audience, prior to an extensive regional tour
and a sold-out stint in Town. Ah... Town!

As I was saying... Scant memory of this house from the street.
Then I came inside... That did precious little for my recall either.
What has the present occupant done to the place! All these dashed
tomes! What is the point in putting up a thing of Beauty, of which the
wealthy owner should be proud and his neighbours must be envious,
only to clutter it with rows of mildewing volumes, distracting to the
eye and troubling to the intellect. Doubtless rarely opened, and
evidently never read. Books in a house, I have always maintained,
produce only two things: Dust and Worms. What does that remind
you of? Yes, indeed: The Grave!

And that is an experience of which I can speak with a great deal more
candour than any of you good people. (Mind you, looking around me,

it's evidently a knowledge which many of you shall be sharing before too long, believe me.)

Somehow, however, in here, beneath all this make-over, there is a glimmer of recognition. I can just about perceive the classical contours of The House That Bob Built. And a very fine house it is too. In 1827 (forty years on from my apotheosis to Architectural Elysium) Sutton's 'Stranger's Guide to Nottingham' (which might very well have been written expressly for me, given my current situation) declared it as: 'An elegant brick building with iron palisades…' (Not any longer!) '…which is said to be… (*Said* to be!) '…one of the best built houses in the town.' (*One* of?)

And then, a hundred and twenty years later, along came…Pevsner! This man whose severe Teutonic taste and modernist sensibility you lot seem to endow with inordinate authority.

> *Nikolaus Pevsner, forget him let's never, sir.*
> *He was equally sanguine, writing or eating a Penguin.*

He's still gabbling away, don't you know? Down there on the nursery slopes… where the clouds are rectilinear… forged from spun concrete… and Ambrosia is served from tins. Anyway… he apparently declared in: 'The Buildings Of England' that this was: 'A True Taylor.' Bromley House was characterised thus: 'Very civilised and not at all provincial…with an elegant, very restrained doorway… and Palladian alternating pediments to the main windows.' (Appreciable these days only if watering eyes are raised above Burger King. By the by who is this Burger, and what, pray, is the realm he rules over?) '…And interiors with charming plaster work…' (Still, possibly, somewhere behind all these dust-attracting volumes.) '…Of a rococo character.'

That word, always applied to my work: Ro-Co-Co! As if I were some Tuscan rooster. Ro-Co-Co!

At least it's still standing. Most of my houses in London town are long gone. All of my wonderful work on the Bank of England has been ignominiously destroyed long since. My masterpiece: The Old Lady Of Threadneedle Street. Perhaps it was the thought of an edifice whose express function and design was to safeguard my hard-earned wealth which brought out the very best in me. Indeed, there were those of my envious contemporaries who liked to put it about that it was the very thought of all the nation's lovely currency which brought out the very best in me. Why should the respect and regard in which I have always held liquid assets be a matter over which I should exhibit any degree of shame?

Consider before you condemn. My father rose from humble stock. A monumental mason. Some would say (and I would do nothing to contradict) that he was the greatest of his day. He could wield a flattering chisel. He could make stone sing. But it must be remarked that as a sculptor he made a very poor squire. Only he never realised that he had become the laughing-stock of Essex. A well-heeled village idiot.

With his coaches... his pompadoured servants... his endless entertaining of local leeching lords, avaricious aristocracy. Oh yes, I learned only too well, at a very early age, the value of living within one's means. For when the time came for a fellow monumentalist to carve my father's own mausoleum Papa had left me nothing save:

A name... A craft... And a pile of mounting bills standing higher than my navel.

So I went to work. In forty years in the profession I never rose from my bed a minute after four o'clock in the morning. I abstained from spiritous liquors. I eschewed animal flesh. And I chose my clients well. I worked for men of business.

New men... Coming men... City men... Government financiers... Army contractors... Respectable merchants... Lawyers... And Bankers. Men like this Smith. Not the most refined of sensibilities I grant you. Men who most likely thought that a *piano nobile* was a costly musical instrument. But men who could Pay Their Way!

Of the first twenty thousand I made through my own hard labours fifteen of them were used to pay off my dear father's (and don't let us forget my loving brother's) debts. Whilst the better part of the remaining five (how can I ever forget?) quickly evaporated through supporting my darling wife's poor relations in a style of life to which they had become suddenly and inextricably accustomed.

So why should it shock you that, when it was my turn to join the choir invisible, I made dashed sure that I did nothing to lumber my own offspring with a lifetime of shuddering at each rise of the door knocker... Dodging creditors... Shaking at the sight of one's own father's ill-considered signature.

One hundred and eighty thousand pounds sterling. Guaranteed by the trustees of the Bank Of England. The Bank that Bob built. *That* was my legacy. And every expendable penny I ever made was put to work as hard as I had worked myself to earn it. For I invested it all in Mortgages on the property of the Aristocracy. Yes, I made those spendthrifts suffer. I made their lordships lament. I made their penurious pips squeak. Believe me.

And then, of all the nerve, *The Times*... (I think I have the yellowing cutting here somewhere on my person...) The Thunderer had the gall to write: 'Such was the late Sir Robert Taylor's *vanity* that he bequeathed one guinea to each little boy and girl that sung at his funeral...' (a decent day's pay for a job well done; what was ever wrong with that?)

'The outward trappings of *useless* expense on this funeral drew together a vast concourse of people...' (what should I have done with my own money?) 'And the crowd of vagabonds and pickpockets was so great at St Martin-in-the-Fields that many of the justices who honoured his corpse with their presence lost their watches, purses and handkerchiefs.' Oh, death where is thy sting?

Nevertheless: One hundred and eighty thousand! Horace Walpole proclaimed, in a far more balanced and considered obit: 'There is no instance in art like it.' Quite right. Wren only managed to bequeath a measly fifty thou. But... (and how can I ever forget?) there remains the question of: Everlasting Eminence! Abiding Glory! Dome Without End, Amen. 'If you want to see his memorial look around you!'

My memories have been largely demolished. I'm looking around me. What do I see? Bromley House! 'Very civilised and not at all provincial.' This was a house that Bob built upon Money. Literally. Old George Smith, that merchant banker. Not that I have any especial memory of him... Possibly obese... Doubtless gouty... Fingers evidently stiff and calloused from all that counting.

George Smith. I'm sure he had his banking hall downstairs. And merchants from the Midlands and the North came here... Depositing their profits... Begging for some extension on their loans. And he would give his 'Yay' or 'Nay'. In this fine house. Five storeys high. Brick-built with Flemish bond and stone ornamentation. The best built house in town. The only books in those days old Smith might stick his snout in: Ledgers. The Profit and the Loss. The Scarlet and the Black.

And then what? (Allow me to speculate.) The banker would have bequeathed the house and the contents of his safe to an over-educated heir in whom his hopes were vainly fixed. And this pampered second-generationalist doubtless would have made a decent match into the gentry and taken on himself the name of his dear wife's aristocratic kin. The Bromleys! (Ah-ha! So that, perhaps, is why this place is denominated Bromley House!) Then this childless ne'er-do-well might have borrowed against his father's hard-won property and his wife's well-regarded name to run up his own, and to pay off his relations' debts. And then, (please indulge this temporary exercise of an

otherwise defunct imagination, but I do know whereof I speak)
George Junior… née simple Smith… now Baronet Bromley… would
have been revealed, uncovered, in a public place, arrested, tried at the
assizes and convicted for committing: 'Vile and unnatural crimes.'
So the house was lost along with reputation.

Merely a stab at circumstance on my part… May or may not have
happened. But I'm sure you'll find it's not so very far from the truth.
Vanity, vanity, all is vanity.

Doubtless the house was auctioned off and bought by a bunch of
unappreciative bookworms, who opened it up to every passing devil
on Angel Row.

And I still don't know whether it's one of mine! Honestly, it's never
been really attributed to me, either in that tedious monograph, nor in
'Country Life.' Truth be told, not even old Pevsner gave me a
thorough-going name-check. Not in the original edition. The one he
wrote himself.

I fear that I may be here under false pretences. It was all so very long
ago. How could you possibly expect me to recall?

Then… On the stairs:

Wait a moment… Come out here! Look up! This might very well be
one of mine! I'd not be in any way ashamed to add this stairwell to the
catalogue raisonée. Who else but myself, the most distinguished British
architect of his day… before that Robert Adam entered the lists.

> *Whose is that naked arse I see,*
> *Exposed to all the gentry?*
> *Whose bare-faced cheeks*
> *Fawn to both Lord and Madam?*
> *G-d damn him, it's that bloody builder: Adam.*

Who else but me, Robert Taylor, could have conceived of this
beautiful domed staircase hall? Who else would have been bold
enough, yet sufficiently restrained, to have crafted this curving
handrail, these barley-sugar balusters, these spandrels?

'Very Civilised…Not At All Provincial.'

> *Robert Taylor, has been dismissed as a failure,*
> *But for those in the know, on Angel Row,*
> *Though never one for shockin' 'em*
> *His work lives on*
> *At Bromley House in Nottingham.*

This *is* a true Taylor! I'm convinced of it!

A WALK THROUGH THE CITY OF NOTTINGHAM WITH WATSON FOTHERGILL, ARCHITECT.

Standing out in proud reproach to the variously dull or downright ugly buildings, which look as if they've been tossed-off without a thought for purpose or location, the works of Fothergill Watson (or Watson Fothergill as he became) enhance the streets of the centre and inner suburbs of my native town. As austere and evangelical in his personal life as he was playful in his professional work, Fothergill was much more than a 'provincial Goth' who flourished at a time when the Gothic Revival was all but out-of-date. His buildings are an eclectic mixture of styles: baronial, Bavarian, vernacular black-and-white of the Tudor age, Queen Anne chimneys, Dutch gables—a stylistic Cook's Tour, yet always constructed from local brick and stone. They are a daring affront to the aesthetic purist who must gasp in horror while the unschooled rest of us sigh in pleasure, our spirits momentarily lifted above the mundane. Even his speculative workers' terraces and alms house for the agèd poor display exuberant and arguably unnecessary additions which raise them above the functional and his warehouses and commercial buildings are ornamented with turrets, fancy wrought iron work, terracotta panelling depicting scenes symbolic of the history of their contemporary use.

In 2004 I was asked by Julian Marsh, a pioneer of ecologically-aware architecture whose own buildings are not devoid of the occasional post-modern metaphorical flourish, if I might contribute to the Royal Institute of British Architects' Architecture Week. I suggested a Fothergill Trail, with Patrick Wildgust personating this architect as he had Robert Taylor. I was charged with the far more significant role of People Management and Traffic Control.

The journey began outside one of Mister Fothergill's earliest domestic commissions in the Park Estate by the side of Nottingham Castle, then wove its way past many of his surviving structures, concluding with the shock of discovery that one of his best-loved and most elaborated buildings, the Black Boy Hotel—whose imposing edifice and labyrinthine interior rooms was well-remembered by Graham Greene from the short time he lived and worked in the city in the late 1920s, even though the name of the establishment was mis-remembered as the 'Black Dog'—was no longer standing. Much to the continuing regret of those of us who also recollect its splendour, one of the glories of the East Midlands had been demolished in 1970 and a loathsome store peddling cut-price clothing was flung up on the site. At the time of the walk this was occupied by Littlewoods and I have chosen to retain that appellation as I couldn't think of any bitter puns on Primark. I fancy that weaving home on certain nights after a session in the boozers of Mansfield Road I have witnessed Fothergill's humble memorial in the Rock Cemetery spinning in disbelief at the violation of his memory. More recently a massive HGV delivering sports ware to another emporium crashed into the small masterpiece of his erstwhile office on George Street, rocking its foundations and bruising its fabric but happily leaving it standing to delight discerning passers-by.

(There are photographs of all the buildings referred to in this monologue, even those now demolished, at the excellent Watson Fothergill Home Page, www.watsonfothergill.co.uk.)

*

OUTSIDE THE HOUSE OF THE MISSES WOODS:

The Architect appears, bewhiskered, attempting to look more distinguished than he may well be, motioning with a stick with an ivory head handle, never quite suppressing his regional accent.

Ah, here we are … Castle Bank. Numbers Five and Seven, Lenton Road, the Park Estate. My first commissioned house. Designed and built in 1873. Nine years after I took up the profession of Architect at the age of twenty-three. Six years after my marriage to my own darling, Anne.

What's that, I hear you say? Who am I? You really have to ask?

Very well. I was born in Mansfield. No need to snigger. I'm well aware of the baneful implication the very name of that outlying market town, so close to the grime of the coal fields, carries here in the county town… painfully aware of the scorn. Should I rather declare that I am a Nottinghamshire Man and proud of it?

My father was a lace merchant—and what more local trade could there be? His family name was Watson, which, again I'm all too aware, is hardly distinguished, being the forty-eighth most common surname in the land. Pa, however, held a profound, sincere and, I confess, possibly unsubstantiated belief that I was descended from aristocratic stock, from my dear mother's side, at least. So I was christened with the name of that distinguished North Country family: the Fothergills.

I stand before you: Fothergill Watson… Or am I Watson Fothergill? But you can me Mister Fothergill… which is how I insist all my office staff and domestic servants must refer to me.

What more do you need to know?

I require exactly seven hours sleep. I systematically take a minimum of two hours walking exercise per diem. I strive to maintain a very straight gait, which I consider somewhat dignified. Height: Five foot ten inches. Weight: Thirteen stones with barely a pound put on since adolescence. Eyes: egg-shell blue. Hair: the once golden locks, silvering now, yet remaining not undistinguished. Eyebrows: dark, well-marked. Mouth: rather small beneath this moustache with the upper lip curled. Forehead: rather high. Chin: very well chiselled.

My dear wife commissioned a portrait of me in oils, painted by Arthur Hill R.A. But it's rather 'unflattering', she asserts, and the complexion, she says and I cannot but agree, is somewhat lifeless looking—which is certainly not to nature, as my appearance has, if I say so myself as shouldn't, always been clear and bright. The artist did not capture my essence and the exercise was a waste of time and money.

However, I have not come to talk about myself, but to show off my work!

Upon examination of these dwellings the discriminating eye can discern, even at this early date in my architectural career, stylistic features which I have made all my own.

Notice the tall, decorated chimney stacks, the classically inflected pillar mullions on this corner window—I always rose to the challenge of a corner—blue tiles, not common slates, on the roofs. And, perhaps most characteristic of all, the horizontal banding of blue bricks of the highest quality and the deepest hue with local stone providing a striking but not unpleasing contrast. Brick! Formed from Nottingham clay. So local, so natural and so popular. Yet, in my hands, so distinctive!

This is what I have always striven for, in a word: Individuality!

You see, in architectural design individuality is the most valuable quality. Would that we had more of it! How else can an architect give character to a building? How else can I stamp my own sensibility? From the very start, I made no concession to the untutored taste of my clients. By approaching me in the first place they already displayed sufficient good judgement to realise my own discernment was far in advance of their own. I never yet met one who was dissatisfied with the outcome.

John Ruskin said in a phrase which has become something of a cliché, that every building should be a 'living creature'. True enough. But, *pace* Ruskin, allow me some mild and well-intentioned criticism of the greatest aesthete of this, or possibly any other age, for he did not go far enough. I would add: Every building should tell a story.

And what story do these well-appointed houses tell? A story of financial security, comfort, firmly established traditions of the household, surely. But also a tale of closeness, the fond attachment between my clients, the Misses Woods. Unmarried sisters, with impeccable taste and the means to achieve it.

Rather understated in view of some of my later works, I grant. But the first of many houses designed by me in the Duke of Newcastle's Park Estate. 1873 was a landmark year for me. For, after nine years of hard work, and a good deal of struggle and frustration, I found business increasing considerably. At last I was thoroughly established.

I am almost a total abstainer. I sometimes go for nearly a year without even tasting strong drink. Perhaps that is why, in that very same year, I put my very heart and soul into the competition for the design of the Temperance Hall. And my proposal won! I would hesitate to say it was my moral rectitude which swayed the judges in my favour. You might know it as the Albert Hall. A magnificent edifice. My first major public building. *The Messiah; Elijah; From Olivet to Calvary*—these and such as these gloriously inspirational works were all performed before audiences of three thousand three hundred souls in an edifice emanating from my imagination, esteemed as (and this is a citation I relish) 'acoustically equal to any concert hall in the kingdom'. The powerful tower, in early French Gothic style, dominated the city's western skyline. A Protestant reproach to Pugin's stern Roman Catholic cathedral across the Derby Road. But, alas, I forget, this is a building which will never be seen. Destroyed by fire in 1906. Ashes to ashes. A pale shadow of the former glory was erected in the wake of my magnificent construction.

Nevertheless, for me it was a great step forward! The Albert Hall made my name.

He strides off and all have to follow at his pace.

OUTSIDE MORTIMER HOUSE:

I have been dubbed, not without some malice: 'A Provincial Goth'. As if my detractors might think I would find either of those terms offensive. On the contrary, I embrace the insult.

How could I ever deny that my work exists in the English provinces of my birth or that my passion for the medieval was engendered when, as a youth, my impressionable mind was transported on visits to the great cathedrals of Lincoln and Southwell? So much did the achievement of those master masons of the Middle Ages stir up my zeal for architecture that I commenced to absorb their inspiration and left no stone unturned in my endeavours to conquer that profession. My enthusiasm has only grown with the years.

The pattern book of the Past should not be considered as a moral blueprint for the Present. Man must worship his Maker with his heart. Bricks and mortar are a mere expression of my philosophy. Certainly, the Gothic is not some religious crusade. The Gothic is a style. Some might say this style is now out of fashion. But I ask you: What other form is best suited to transform abstract thought into concrete structure? What other template can furnish us with such an inexhaustible mine of novelty and variety? This is a living language capable of infinite expression. Though in these times it may languish, the Gothic is not dead, only sleeping and it will return. Believe me!

Mind you, the ignorant who label me a 'Goth' severely circumscribe my influences and entirely misunderstand my purpose.

Have a look at Mortimer House designed by me in 1883. Commissioned as a row of commercial shops and offices on a prime sight opposite the gatehouse of the recently restored Nottingham Castle. Once a fortress for royal despots in the days of yore and gore. Then the habitation of hard-hearted noblemen. Now, in these more enlightened times, a place of beauty and tranquility where the working classes can mingle with lovers of the fine and decorative arts to venture freely for recreation and edification.

The restoration of the Castle was entrusted to my eminent colleague Thomas Hine. No, let us be honest, he was ever my rival and continual thorn in my side. Beloved by the City Fathers, old Hine was gifted all the most prestigious sites and churned out his characteristically uncontentious second-rate draughtsmanship, offending none, surprising nobody, signifying nothing. Only imagine what I could have made with our most significant structure, languishing above the city since the rioters of the Reform Bill had laid it waste. Where once the Sheriff of Nottingham had exercised his tyrannical rule. Where Robin Hood in legend won the Silver Arrow in a contest of archery and rescued Little John from its deep dark dungeons. Visualise how my imagination might have presided over romantic renovation. For this was where King Edward the Second came up through the sandstone caves and burst upon his mother, Queen Isabella, in the arms of the pretender Roger Mortimer…

Well, it was not to be. If I'd have had my way the Castle would not have looked like some trumped-up magnate's mansion. My modest revenge was Mortimer House. In the shadow of the Castle but far more interesting than anything Hine came up with.

Consider my response to a very tricky site. If the uphill terrain is asymmetrical, so must be the design. Look at the varied line of the roofs contrasting with the straight horizontal of the blue bricks. Allow your eye to travel pleasingly from the square tower down to the round turret. Is this the work of a 'provincial Goth'? Is this an Olde English parody? Is this some half-cocked derivative of Northern French vernacular? The only pertinent questions are: Is it not perfectly suited to its location? And is it ever the slightest bit dull? Howsoever my critics might wish to describe this building, it is surely a genuine Fothergill.

He's off again. Down Castle Gate towards the city centre.

ON CASTLE GATE:

Let us pause here awhile to look over this town. The place I have made my own.

Once known as 'the Garden City' Nottingham became, by the time of my birth in 1841, one of the most fetid, disease-ridden, over-populated places in this country, if not, indeed, the British empire. At the time I began my career nearly eighty seventy thousand souls were crowded into less than two thousand acres. Then, in 1877, a transformation! The passage of the Extension Act which brought the outlying parishes into the borough extending the area five-fold. Nottingham was suddenly wide-open for development for those lucky few who possessed the means.

And then, in the very same year, 1877: A reversal of Fortune! My dear wife Anne's father, a wholesale brewer (yes, from Mansfield before you scoff) passed over bequeathing his only daughter, my darling: Forty Thousand Pounds!

Out of the strong came sweetness... as it says on the Tate and Lyle treacle tin beside the picture of an expired lion in a biblical quotation from the Book of Judges.

Thus it was that my wife and I began buying freehold land around the new, enlarged borough to let out as ninety-nine year leases—the very safest form of investment. In the following decades buildings were erected at the rate of over two thousand five hundred per annum. Many of them were mine!

My growing reputation led to ever more commissions to design fine villas for the wealthy lace and textile merchants and industrialists of this thriving community. But I was not so imprudent as to place all the eggs in one basket. I also began to design well-built terraced houses for the working population. Homes any honest artisan would be proud to inhabit.

On speculation. Very profitable speculation, as it turned out.

No surprise as my commercial skills had been anticipated from an early age. My dear father was a convinced advocate of Phrenology—an apparent science which maintains that character traits can be determined by an examination of the shape of the skull. Therefore, when I was but five years old, Pa commissioned a Phrenological Character from Professor E. T. Craig—though from what seat of learning he had graduated it is perhaps best not to inquire. After passing his practised hands over my childish head's bumps, he reported:

> *He will be prudent, worldly and calculating and disposed to accept value for value, yet always governed by a sense of justice and a regard for the opinions of others. Fond of planning and conniving, he will be: The Man Of Business!*

I'm not saying I put any especial faith in phrenology… But it does make you think!

He's off again towards the Old Market Square.

QUEEN'S CHAMBERS OFF THE MARKET SQUARE:

If this town was going to change then I was determined to be instrumental in the metamorphosis. Come, let me show you!

Look north from this our Market Square, one of the largest public spaces in these isles. Attempt, if your fancy is sufficiently developed, to conjure up in your mind's eye what once was here: the festering warrens, the miasmic breeding grounds of typhoid, of cholera, of smallpox to scar the face of The Queen Of The Midlands.

The Rookeries!

Ah, what terrible images those syllables evoke to those who can recall those pestilent passages, those courts of contagion. Would that this town had produced a laureate who could picture in mere words the vile stench provoked by the ordure, human and animal, which flowed from these malignant alleys. And no less putrid the moral odour emanating from the barely-human inhabitants. Draining from these slums. Rising up as an affront to Heaven. A continual reproach to our municipality:

But, in 1881, the Rookeries were cleared, and broad thoroughfares laid out upon the site. Cleanliness replacing filth. Honest commerce replacing foul vice. Bringing Light out of Darkness.

Over there: Market Street. And King Street and Queen Street, in their distinctive Y-shaped pattern. With Waterhouse's Prudential Buildings providing the focal point.

What could better signal the extent of this transformation than an edifice dedicated to Assurance for a new breed of sober, law-abiding townsfolk, now ever-mindful of their future? But if it was to be the blood-red brick of a London architect which would lead the eye up out of the square, then surely it should be the more vernacular vision of a local man whose design would supplant the citizen back into the commercial and political hub.

And who around here could compete with… Mister Fothergill?

Queen's Chambers. On yet another difficult and convoluted corner site! Erected in 1897, the year of Her Majesty's Diamond Jubilee—the year that Nottingham was at last granted the status of a City.

Carefully chosen elements of my distinctive repertoire out on parade! Who would dare dub me a vulgar Goth when faced with this Tudor black-and-white half-timbering; these thrusting Elizabethan bay windows; these soaring Stuart chimneys; this Baronial tower. Ornamentation reminiscent of regal forebears to honour a royal lady.

In the very heart of this City. In the very heart of England. In the very heart of Empire.

And there she is, looking down upon us: The face of Her Majesty!

Now, there are those who have mis-characterised this sculpture as an ungracious portrait due to the smallness of size and tucked-away position. What a calumny! True enough, the eye has to search for her. But I myself consider this a humble tribute to a great lady. What did they expect: A statue? We already have one over there at the foot of Market Street… Oh no, it seems to have disappeared!

I stand unrivalled in my affection and respect for Our Queen Empress who endowed the very age in which I have lived and prospered with her own dear name. The Victorian Era. The reign over which she has presided has been an age of Progress and Prosperity; of Trade and of Tranquillity; of Freedom and the Family. And I am proud to call myself a true Victorian!

Perhaps her greatest legacy has been, not her imperial expansion, but her domestic arrangements, which have provided an inspiration for every right-thinking Englishman. Our own seven children: Young Fothergill, Anne, Edith, Eleanor, Marian, Clarice and Harold… Our own Princes and Princesses (well, all apart from young Harold, the black sheep of the family, the miscreant, always in some pickle or other… every home must have one, so I'm assured).

Our own well-appointed villa on Mapperley Road. A microcosmic Windsor! Ruskin, again, described the family home as so eloquently as ever:

> *Built to last and built to be lovely, with such differences as might suit and express each man's character, occupation and history, raising the habitation to a kind of monument.*

And our's is the snuggest of houses! This is what we aimed at: comfort and not great cold rooms with gems of art sparkling around. Were you to be there now, as an honoured guest, you might upon entering the hallway cast a glance at the oil painting of Lilith with a snake coiled around her lithesome form. And above the hearth in the parlour you would be aware of the stuffed head of a stag shot in the Scottish Highlands looking down upon you. You could not fail to notice how rich and comfortable is the warm brown wood ceiling or the floral decoration over the arches with the inscription: *'He that striveth for the mastery is temperate in all things.'*

A quotation, as I'm sure you are aware, from Saint Paul's First Epistle to the Corinthians, which has been my abiding motto. Our house lacks but age. A few ancestral traditions attached would perhaps render it more dear… No, indeed, it could not be more dear. We unbuckle our armour here. We have no secrets within our home. We can all trust one another that, keen as may be the darts shot at each here, yet, when outside and in the world, the family shows a bold front and wards off from its numbers any arrows aimed from a foreign bow. Truly, I consider myself as the *fons et origo* of a truly Victorian family.

Who would deem this domestic portrait 'unflattering'?

Four years after Queen's Chambers, my humble homage to her name and glory, it was my sad privilege to attend Victoria's funeral. I took the Midland Train from Nottingham at eight thirty-two ante meridian and found a good seat on Pall Mall for a guinea. The coffin on a gun carriage was preceded by bands who played airs composed by Beethoven and Chopin, as desired by the Queen, whilst a new King for a new century followed closely behind, looking thoroughly himself. All most impressive. I returned to Nottingham at four fifty-five post meridian, well satisfied with the day and feeling I had done my patriotic duty to be present on such an august occasion.

And he's striding up the road, barely pausing for breath.

AT THE TOP OF KING STREET:

If ever proof were needed that I am no mere plunderer of the past, but a thoroughly Modern Man, constructing buildings for the present age, working with modern materials and modern methods for The Modern City… then look across at our premier department store. A pure and formal solution for an entirely modern problem: Shopping.

This sturdy superstructure of cast iron and concrete designed to deliver inviting open spaces, to display the wants and wares, for The Modern Woman. Yes, I supplied my utilitarian patrons with their warehouses, their offices, their shops. But raise your eyes to see how much more I gave them! How could I resist the carved Bavarian woodwork which had so impressed me on my first continental journey? Look at this this characteristically imposing tower, barely visible from street level. Extraneous embellishments? Surely not! Distinct and distant enticements when approaching the town. Declaring: Come inside and purchase.

Inappropriate for Nottingham? No! Should Beauty be out-of-place anywhere? Even here? Buildings must speak of their purpose, their function.

Come along! Come along! Time is running out! There is so much more for you to see.

He's away down Parliament Street, the central thoroughfare.

NOTTINGHAM EXPRESS OFFICES:

If we linger long on Parliament Street, then as now, the city's busiest thoroughfare, I can take no responsibility as to your personal safety from the press of passing carriages and public transportation. I trust you are prudently covered... by Waterhouse's Prudential Assurance perhaps? But I cannot let you rush past, like all the rest of this unseeing crowd, the offices of the Nottingham Express and Journal. In the land of the blind the one-eyed man is... Run Out Of Town!

Extra! Extra! News! News! Encountered... Written... Sub-Edited... Type-set... Printed. Onto the wagons and out on the streets. All in one building. My building.

Another practical response entirely. Functional, yet not devoid of ornamentation!

For the Express was of a Liberal bent. And so I gave them busts of Gladstone, Cobden, Bright. Heroes of the Whigs who ran this paper! Unnecessary Decoration? Or rather: Vital Expression?

But even I am hard pressed to satisfy your curiosity as to why there is a tower. And why, jutting out from the roof line, I gave them gargoyles. Are they not simply decorative whimsy?

I'm sure I must have had a rationale... It was so long ago.

Ah, yes! Can we not say that in today's accelerated world the press, the organ of communication towers above the skyline, serving the role once played by the medieval cathedral. Will that suffice for explanation?

Truth be told, I'd always had an itch to offer gargoyles as I like the look of them! By making too many sacrifices to utilitarianism the nobility of your design will suffer. Who among you would calumniate me for the inclusion of these grotesque beasts?

In years to come there will be those who make a special visit and declare that my work is what makes Nottingham Nottingham.

But before we go further allow me to pose a conundrum. I received this commission in 1875 shortly after the Albert Hall, when my star was firmly on the rise. And you may have noticed the initials of the architect etched proudly and appropriately upon this portal: F. W. Fothergill Watson.

Nearly a quarter of a century later, however, the owners of this expanding newspaper wished for a fourth storey. There... it's not difficult to see the join. For, though the original building was raised in local stone, the addition is in good quality red brick. And you would have to admit that the later architect has performed this tiresome task with some sensitivity and not a little panache, would you not?

His name, too, is immortalised upon this building. High up on the extension there is a sandstone plaque which reads: Watson Fothergill!

Who was this interloper? Why has he not only stolen my initials but reversed my very names? Patience. All will be revealed!

And he's off again, leading the coterie further down the thoroughfare.

STATION BUILDINGS, PARLIAMENT STREET:

With a Fothergill, you never got what you'd bargained for. Put it another way: You *always* got what *I* bargained for!

I never gave the public what they wanted. For it is my profound belief that they deserve far better than that. I gave them what they hadn't even imagined, what they could never even desire until they saw. A Vision Realised!

That's the role of the Professional.

You see, if I were asked to design, say, Alms Houses for Distressed Gentlefolk, they'd find dark wooden porches, oriel windows, and fancy filials on the rooftops.

And if I were to submit a blue-print for a row of Workers' Cottages, then the bricks fronting the street would be hard-fired, long-lasting, shiny-red with a strong course of blue bricks proudly distinguishing their terrace from those of their neighbours spewed out by the yard by fling-'em-up Speculative Builders.

Station Buildings, 1896. Nothing out of the ordinary. The Great Central Railway from Nottingham Victoria to London Marylebone shakes the foundations as trains run below. But see these four terracotta panels depicting Eastern scenes: 'Men Plying Sampans'; 'A Far Eastern Market'; 'Cutting Sugar Cane'; 'Boiling Sugar Cane'.

Another instance of unnecessary decoration? But I predict: One day they'll be coming to this city from China! And the people of Nottingham will be visiting the Far East. Hard to imagine, I know. But if they do they will always and already have an image of a World Beyond Their World.

You have been introduced to a sampling of my works, but the best is yet to come.

Perhaps it is time you learnt more about me, not as an Architect but as a Man. I can do no better than share with you a reading of my palm when I consulted the celebrated psychic Mademoiselle Estelle—the only Parisian yet encountered with a Lancastrian brogue, but no matter, some of her aperçus proved not entirely inaccurate.

'Had you had more confidence in your own abilities you would have done far better than you have…'
(I did well enough, thank you very much, but could I have reached further, could I have worked on a larger stage?)
'I judge your calling to be something commercial…'
(Warm, to a degree.)
'Or that of a physician…'
(No, no. Cold… very chilly.)
'Ah, the commercial so thoroughly enters into your life…'
(Yes, yes. But what about the artistic?)
'You may take a part in some literary composition…'
(Way off.)
'You can adapt yourself readily to people of whatever grade in life and enter into their feelings and plans…'
(More like it! I'd like to think so.)
'You are good at giving information and instruction to others.'
(I pride myself upon that, though it has been said of me that I am rather stern on a building site and it is true that I never wish to communicate directly with the workmen… Does that not betoken proper practice between men and their master rather than stand-offishness or snobbery?)
'But firm determination sometimes becomes obstinacy…'
(It has been said and what's wrong with that, pray? I know they would laugh behind my back when I was wont to inspect details with a dentist's mirror, but I consider that thoroughness and perfectionism.)
'Fresh ideas are always arising and presenting themselves…'
(That's more like it!)
'You trust your own judgement and are not guided by other people…'
(Never!)
'Though you are inclined to be vain…'
(Some truth there, I must admit. I always dressed in winter months in a fur collared overcoat topped off with a silk hat and, in the summer, in loose, decorous linen, and I was conveyed from my house every day in my carriage and four… But, for a man of my standing, it's necessary to maintain standards; I could hardly appear in brown overalls, could I?)
'At the age of eleven a death occurred which had a great effect upon you…'
(Amazing! How could she know? My poor father!)
'At nineteen years of age another death which had still more influence upon you…'
(Uncanny, my dearest mother!)

'At twenty-four a great change in your life occurred...'
(Marriage! I'm beginning to believe.)
'You are an admirer of pretty faces...'
(Assure my dear wife, only on canvas.)
'And beauty in every shape.'
(If she'd only mentioned my love of cricket Mademoiselle Estelle would have
bowled me out for a duck. Owzat!)

I'm not saying that I put any especial faith in palmistry.... But it does make
you think!

Off around the corner onto Pelham Street.

NOTTINGHAM AND NOTTS. BANK:

A Bank... I did a few. But, then again, too few to mention. Except, perhaps,
for the Nottingham and Notts. Bank. Another early commission. A drawn-
out drama, built between 1877 and 1882. Rather Italianate in inspiration, I'd
venture. A sermon in sawn stone from the quarries of Nottinghamshire.
If every decent building expresses a hidden message what is this story if not:
Security and Permanence?

The panelling depicts the wealth upon which this county is based and the
trade of the town: Agriculture, Textiles and Mining. And, see, I did manage
to smuggle in my little joke: A monkey! If we were able to go inside the
banking hall I'd be able to show you another of his simian cousins with a
chain around his neck.

Why aren't you laughing? Ah, perhaps you do not know that in my day being
in thrall to a mortgage is like having a monkey on your back. Wit... Or what?

This is the last work you will see by: 'Fothergill Watson—Architect'.

Now it's time to witness the abiding glory of: 'Watson Fothergill—Architect.'

He strides away towards George Street.

THE OFFICE:

My poor mercantile father's profound, sincere belief that my dear mother's
family was of noble blood, and that, therefore, his son, myself, was separated
from the Common Herd, has led me, solely on his departed behalf, upon a
quest for aristocratic substantiation.

To this end I have expended considerable resources in securing the services of a Genealogical Researcher who has, not without a degree of doubt and uncertainty, traced the roots of our family tree back to William the Conqueror. Proving to my satisfaction that I am: an indisputable Fothergill. Therefore, in 1893, I took a step which has for many years been contemplated: I changed my name by deed poll, which in my own case meant a simple transposition.

No longer: Fothergill Watson. I became... Watson Fothergill!

For business reasons I did not wish the name to look so very different. I was known by one and all, as I already told you, Mister Fothergill... which is, unlike the common 'Watson', one of the most unusual surnames in the land! So in that very same year, in 1893, I acquired a new name and constructed a new office.

This is ME! In bricks and mortar and local stone. If you want to see my monument: Look around you!

Here I honoured my Masters.

Augustus Webley Northmore Pugin—a great, ungainsayable 'Goth', though hardly 'provincial'. There are malicious tongues who have suggested that I positioned this bust with some degree of deliberation so that his back is turned away from his own R.C. cathedral on Derby Road. Ridiculous! What if I had positioned him in the opposite direction? It would not be his *face* looking out upon us now!

George Edmund Street—there are those critics who reckon my bank was an *homage* (though they preferred a ruder term) to his imposing Law Courts on The Strand. But I rejoin: Where else could I resist memorialising George Street except here... On George Street?

George Gilbert Scott—sublime artist of the Albert Memorial, Saint Pancras Station and, nearer to home, Kelham Hall. A deep-dyed Goth if ever there was one!

William Burges—could it be from his love of the medieval that I learnt the glory of the gargoyle?

And Norman Shaw—who inspired me with the contrasting beauty of the black and the wonder of the white.

I am humble enough to acknowledge my influences. And proud enough to know that it was my imagination which cast them in the refiner's fire and with what emerged I made all my own.

Not for nothing am I known as 'eclectic'—another epithet which damns me with faint praise. In the hands of some meeker, less audacious talent these architectural languages might have produced a shrieking Tower of Babel. But see how here they all conjoin to engender Harmony and Delight. Unexpected Combination produces True Inspiration!

For here, on my own frontage, I demonstrate my antecedents.

And presiding over all: The Ideal Type of the very man to whom I aspire. No, not my own figure, I am not that vainglorious, though my signature does adorns the frontage. But a statue of The Architect!

My office was a present to myself. Each day as I arrived for work I could see my own countenance reflected in this polished marble façade... Mind you, I also sub-let the ground floor to a shop-keeper which covered all my costs.

The Artist! The Business Man! Why should these two warring souls not be incarnated in the same person?

He leads his followers back to Long Row, at the side of Council House.

AT THE SITE OF THE ERSTWHILE BLACK BOY:

Now, before we say farewell, I wish to display my present to the people of Nottingham. My supreme glory. Look out for the massive central tower, the wooden gables, the Bavarian balcony which makes The Black Boy Hotel the talk of all the town. The jewel in my crown.

I am a Nottingham man and proud of it. How would this place have looked had I not stamped my seal upon the city?

But he is pole-axed when he sees that the Black Boy Hotel is no longer there.

Where is it? What have they done with it? Gone? Destroyed! Without a word of protest! Littlewoods? Little Heart! Little Soul! Do they not care? Could it be that the purpose of my life has all been a vain dream? My fondest desire was to bring beauty into an ugly world and look where it has led.

Only one design remains on my drawing board, one last blueprint. The simplest of them all. Executed in rough-hewn sandstone… Mansfield stone. No decoration. No elaboration. Only a name. What is my name? FW or WF? My own humble memorial in the Rock Cemetery… out of the city on the road to Mansfield. My body will be turning in my grave as my small soul commences that great journey. From Darkness unto Light. No client but that Great Architect who moulded us out of the clay from which we were formed and to which we are destined to return.

He walks away and is lost in the crowd.

Watson Fothergill

DRELLA AND THE MACGUFFIN.

Of the (many) unmade screenplays I've written *Drella and the MacGuffin* is the one I would have most wished to see move from Development Hell into Production Purgatory—Exhibition Elysium would be far too much to expect. BBC Scotland had made a series of dramas, 'Encounters', about meetings between famous people. When Bill Bryden, then Head of Drama, asked me whom I would select for the opening episode of the second series I didn't have to think for long. Pinned to my wall was a postcard capturing the only meeting between Andy Warhol and Alfred Hitchcock, taken when Andy quizzed Alfred for his Interview Magazine in September 1974. There could not be two

Alfred Hitchcock and Andy Warhol

film-makers with less in common than Andy and Hitch—apart from the fact they were both Catholics. Warhol would typically turn on the camera and allow his performers to do what they would while he went off to make a phone call with the take ending when the film ran out, whilst Hitch planned every shot meticulously before filming and created suspense through montage, perhaps most famously in the shower scene from *Psycho* with its 52 cuts in 45 seconds. And yet I had loved the work of both of these very different auteurs since my teens. I became fascinated with the bizarre troupe of 'superstars' which coagulated around Andy when I first saw *Chelsea Girls* at Trent Polytechnic film club and, like every wannabe film-maker, I studied Hitch's work, often having to go to Paris to track down the more obscure titles on VHS in those days before internet availability. By the time I went to live in New York in 1976 Andy had stepped back from the excesses of his previously outré lifestyle but I was lucky enough to meet some of the radioactive half-life of the 60s Factory and the magnificent Ondine became a close friend, furnishing me with his cast-off clothing to protect me from the bitter Manhattan winter. Though I never met Hitchcock, of course, I was introduced to his daughter, Patricia, when she was in Nottingham on the 14th of August 1999 to unveil a plaque honouring her brilliant mother, Alma Reville, who was born a century earlier on Robin Hood Chase.

In that improbable encounter Warhol talked of the assassination attempt made on him by Valerie Solanas in 1968: 'Well, I was shot by a gun and it just seems like a movie. I can't see it as being anything real. The whole thing is still like a movie to me. It happened to me, but it's like watching TV. If you're watching TV, it's the same thing as having it done to yourself.'

This characteristic remark provided my approach: Hitch was making an episode of his TV series, *Alfred Hitchcock Presents*, in which the Pope of Pop was shot, but he survived—which was not in the script. So the Master of Suspense has to find another way to tell the story... This provided a structural framework which could dramatize their entirely dissimilar ways of working as well as allowing me to pay *homage* to their peculiar film practices. The script was written. The series was launched with free drinks and canapés in the Groucho Club.

And then... nothing!

In 1999, the centenary of Hitchcock's birth (he was born the day before his wife and constant collaborator) I gathered a bunch of chums and reworked it as a live show. The first outing was at the National Film Theatre when the electrical system packed up making our elaborate multi-media presentation redundant—what else can you expect from London's most prestigious cinema venue? We reprised it more successfully at the Broadway Cinema in Nottingham and I later did readings as part of the Hitchcock exhibition at the Museum of Modern Art, Sydney and, most gratifyingly, at a conference at the Andy Warhol Museum in his native Pittsburgh.

*

1. EXT/INT. NEW YORK STREET SET/FACTORY. DAY. (B&W)

A hand-held cinema verité style swoop off the sidewalk of a
obviously studio version of a New York street into the dingy
lobby of a commercial building. PEOPLE come and go dressed
in 1968 styles and, as the POV wobbles towards a large
service elevator, a SHADOWY FIGURE slides into the lift.

A glimpse is caught of a rotund MAILMAN with a cart filling the
letter boxes against the wall of the lobby. He turns momentarily.

He is ALFRED HITCHCOCK making his cameo performance.

The grilled doors of the elevator slam shut as the music begins:

> VELVET UNDERGROUND SONG
> *We're gonna have a real good time together,*
> *We're gonna have a real good time together.*
> *Na na na-na na na, na-na na-na naaaa...*

As the elevator rises a jumble of letters appear, spinning
around, forming anagrammatic words and phrases. Such as:

HAND HELD FANCY ART CHIC - OLD DRACULA FILM —
DEATH FANG WINNER OK.

OH HELL — CHALK FACED CAN ART — FUDDY NNW DIRECTOR
HAD ANGINA.

TECHNICAL HAD FRENCH DRINK AT ILL GRAY DAWN — OH
LEAD ON MACDUFF.

ANAGRAM: CHANCE, FAITH AND LADY LUCK DIRECT WORLD.

Eventually they coalesce into:

> ANDY WARHOL AND ALFRED HITCHCOCK
> IN
> DRELLA AND THE MacGUFFIN.

The wobbly shot and the music continue as the elevator
doors are opened and that shadowy figure, breathing heavily
now, strides through a large studio space. This is The
Factory, in which what can be glimpsed of the walls, the
steam pipes, all the surfaces are painted silver or covered
in aluminium foil.

At the end of the room a slight, fey figure dressed in a
black leather jacket with a platinum blonde wig sits behind
a desk with a phone crooked into his neck shifting Polaroid

photos around the desk top as a tape recorder rolls to
immortalise the call.

He is ANDY WARHOL.

> ANDY *(over the phone)*
> Oh you didn't...? You did...? You slut! You spend
> too much time on your back and not enough time on
> your hair.

He looks up and sees the figure before him, obviously not
unused to the sight of crazies walking in and out of his space.
But then the figure holds forward a brown grocery bag in her
left hand and begins rifling in it with her right, searching
through the candy bars and bags of potato chips to remove a
giant hand gun (not unlike the one at the end of *Spellbound*).
She points the revolver directly at Andy's chest.

> ANDY
> No, no. Don't do it!

She fires once. He hits the floor. She fires four more shots:
two direct hits, two glancing blows.

> ANDY
> I can't...I can't breathe...

> FADE TO BLACK

2. INT. RAILWAY COMPARTMENT SET. DAY. (COLOUR)

Over the theme tune of the television series *Alfred Hitchcock
Presents,* Gounod's *Funeral March of the Marionettes:*

> FADE UP ONTO:

An obviously constructed set of an old-fashioned British
railway compartment, built with scant regard for anything more
than cartoon realism and which would aspire to fool no-one
that this is anywhere else than on the sound stage of a studio.
The figure of a large balding man with a pendulous lower lip,
Alfred Hitchcock, sits snoozing. He is dressed in a safari
suit, the khaki shorts cut so far below the knee that they
almost meet the tops of his knee-length socks, the waist band
hiked up above the impressive sag of a well-tended belly. On
his head he sports a solar topée and in one dozing hand there
resides a huge butterfly net whilst the other supports a
crumpled copy of the London Times. On the sagging luggage rack
opposite his seat in the empty carriage is a leather trunk,

plastered with world-wide traveller's labels. Once he is aware
that all eyes are upon him he awakes and turns to the camera,
addressing it directly in a strange, idiosyncratic voice that
bears the unmistakable vowel sounds of his native East London
unconquered by an attempt at the non-descript accent of the
parvenu Englishman abroad.

                         ALFRED
      Good Evening...

      I was travelling on the sleeper to Inverness when
      a man in the compartment pointed to the luggage
      rack. 'And what have you got in there?' he
      inquired of me, dispensing entirely with the
      formality of an introduction. I answered: 'It's a
      MacGuffin,' and turned back to 13 across: 'Spare
      him not, revolved the man hater.'

      I was just about to write in 'misanthrope', when
      he persisted: 'And what's that for?' With that
      infinite forbearance drummed into me in childhood
      by the whalebone straps of the Jesuits I told him:
      'It's for hunting lions in the Scottish Highlands.'
      'But there are no lions in the Scottish Highlands,'
      he told me. 'Well, then,' I said, cutting off all
      further conversation 'I don't suppose I shall be
      needing my MacGuffin.'

      I'm afraid that—in spite of my best intentions—
      tonight's story does not involve a murder.
      But please do not change the channel, I beg you.
      I realise that violent death is what you've come
      to expect me to deliver into your living rooms.
      Believe me, I did what I could to arrange it for
      you. But now I find myself bereft not only of a
      victim, but also of an investigation, a revelation,
      a twist to the tale and a satisfying climax
      involving a chase through the galleries of the
      Museum of Modern Art. In fact, I'm beginning to
      fear that tonight's story will not turn out to be
      a story at all. And that, ladies and gentlemen,
      will not please My Sponsor.

      So while I continue to wrestle with this enigma
      please enjoy that portion of the show to which
      My Sponsor tells me you should pay the closest
      attention.

                          124

Cover with a caption, white letters on black:

FADE TO BLACK:

3. INT. HOSPITAL SET. NO TIME.
(B & W SLOWLY TURNING TO MUTED COLOUR)

Fade up to a hospital room: greying white walls, black
draped windows, an elaborate crucifix above a single bed
with a little table beside it and a large TV set in the
corner, a cardiac monitor blipping away quietly. On the bed
lies the comatose figure of Andy, neither dead nor alive,
tubes coming out of his side. His wig has been removed
revealing thin greying blonde hairs. (A static shot that
provokes memories of his early films like *Sleep* and *Couch*.)
Slowly he comes into consciousness, his eyelids flicker open
and he tries to look around the room in total
incomprehension gradually turning to horror. When he sees
the drain coming out of his side his neck lurches forward,
causing sudden indescribable pain. On the bedside table he
can see a bell and a television remote control. He slowly
and painfully reaches out with his right hand to pick up the
bell and, with all the force he can muster, shakes it
violently: no sound emerges. He looks at it and tries again:
still silence.

He puts down the bell and reaches out for the remote switch —
he can't quite make it. He stretches his fingers out to
their fullest extent, but it still just eludes him. He picks
up the bell and with its handle slowly moves the switch
toward him finally managing to get a grip on it. He points
it at the TV set in the corner and pushes a button. The TV
set comes to life, but all he gets is static monochrome.
With increasing desperation, he moves through the channel
selection: static everywhere.

ANDY *(v/o)*
Where am I? What's happening? What is all this
snow? I must be in Canada!

He holds back the remote and as its electric eye falls upon
his face the snow clears and an image appears on the TV
screen: extreme close-up details of his own face.

CUT AWAY TO:

4. CLOSE ON TV SCREEN.

Andy's blotchy albino face. Over this:

> ANDY *(v/o)*
> Ugh. What station's this?
> Look at those pimples.
> What is this... the Ugly, Ugly Show?

As the remote plays over his side on the TV set is shown: the crumpled white sheet, dissolving into blood-stained hospital dressings, dissolving into stitched, scarred and suppurating wounds. Over this:

> ANDY *(v/o)*
> Oh gee. That's so beautiful. It looks like zippers on a Dior dress.

Then his whole face is revealed:

> ANDY *(v/o)*
> Oh no! It's me. Why didn't anybody tell me I was going to be on TV? I always wanted my own show. I'd call it *Nothing Special.*

Then he suddenly notices something really shocking and his hand flies up to his head as he gasps audibly.

> ANDY *(v/o)*
> Where is it? What have they done with my wig? It's my worst nightmare: I get my TV show and somebody steals my wig.

> CUT BACK TO:

5. INT. HOSPITAL ROOM. AS BEFORE.

Andy rings the bell again:

> ANDY
> Nurse! Nurse!

Once again the bell makes no sound but on the TV screen appears the unmistakable image of Hitchcock, now dressed as a typical English butler of the Edwardian era, holding a silver platter on which resides a freshly ironed tabloid newspaper.

> ALFRED
> You rang, sir?

6. TV/HOSPITAL.

The next sequence is played cross-cutting between Hitchcock
on TV and Andy in the hospital bed framed so that the gory
crucifix is behind him (reminiscent of the scene between
Norman Bates and Marion Crane in *Psycho*)

                    ANDY
     Who are you?

                    ALFRED *(from the TV set)*
     I might well ask the same.

                    ANDY
     Everybody knows me... I'm A.

                    ALFRED
     A.? I was looking for an Andrei Warhola.

                    ANDY
     Andy Warhol — it sounds more American. I dropped
     the A. Well, I guess I kept it, in a way. I don't
     like to throw anything out. All my friends call me
     A... Or Drella.

Hitchcock looks blank.

                    ANDY
     It was a name given to me by Ondine... One of my
     Superstars. It's means... like... Dracula crossed
     with Cinderella. Because I only come out at night
     and I always get to go to the ball.

                    ALFRED
     I take it this is you in the newspaper?

Hitchcock holds up New York Daily News tabloid showing the
famous splash: *ACTRESS SHOOTS ARTIST—50/50 Chance Doctors Say*.

Andy grabs the newspaper:

                    ANDY
     Oh gee, I made the front page.

                    ALFRED
     Then I *am* in the right place.

Then Andy clocks the headline:

                    ANDY

'Actress Shoots Artist'. Oh no — Valerie Solanas.
It was that flake who shot me? And they gave her
top billing!

                    ALFRED

Once again the gentlemen of the press have
displayed their usual inaccuracy.

                    ANDY

You can say that again: 'Actress'!

                    ALFRED

I was thinking more of 'Artist'.

                    ANDY

What are you talking about? I'm an artist. I make
Art. I am Art! Even my scars are Art. Gee, my
scars, what happened to me?

                    ALFRED

Two bullets entered your body... puncturing your
liver, spleen...

                    ANDY

What about my leather jacket?

                    ALFRED

...Pancreas, oesophagus...

                    ANDY

Where's that?

                    ALFRED

...one pulmonary artery and both your lungs.

                    ANDY

And I survived all that?

                    ALFRED

Did you hear me mention survival? Fifty/fifty
chance doctors say.

Andy suddenly begins to panic.

                    ANDY

What is all this? What are you doing here? Who are
you anyway?

                    ALFRED

You mean to say you don't know?

ANDY

Sure I know: you're B. I'm A and everybody else is
B. I run the whole gamut: from A to B and back
again. I know you're one of the Bs. I just don't
know what kind of B you are.

ALFRED

Let me help you: Who's the most famous film
director in the world?

ANDY

What is this, the Sixty-Four Thousand Dollar
Question? Ordinarily I just adore game shows, but
right now... Anyway, I am.

ALFRED

You?

ANDY

In Manhattan my name's always above the title.

ALFRED

You mean you've never heard of *Alfred Hitchcock
Presents*?

Andy's panic is completely allayed by the presence of
celebrity. He looks hard at the face on the screen —
it is him!

ANDY

Oh gee! An interviewer in Rome once asked me who was
my favourite movie director. Know what I told him?

ALFRED

I should certainly hope so.

Andy's panic returns.

ANDY

Now will you tell me... please, for the love of
God...

ALFRED

I'm afraid I serve a somewhat Higher Power.
My Sponsor expects me to deliver a story every
week. It's in my contract. That's why I'm here.

Andy is suddenly very angry in a petulant, childish sort of way.

ANDY

And you've come to *me* for one of your stories?
What do I know from stories? Stories are from
yesterday. Your show should be called *Alfred
Hitchcock Pasts*. In the future there won't be any
more stories. In the future everybody'll have
machines like tape-recorders and you can just copy
old movies and fast forward through all the boring
scenes where people like talk and do things and
then freeze them at your golden moments, like when
Janet Leigh gets into the shower, or like when
that dykey housemaid combs Joan Fontaine's hair.
And you can hold it right there and just look at
the moments you want to freeze forever. It'll be
like Do It Yourself movies. Like my movies. And we
won't need your dumb stories any more. I don't
want a story, I want a Picture. Stories have
beginnings and endings and I don't know where to
begin and I hate endings. My movies never have
beginnings or endings. My movies start when I turn
on the camera and end when the film runs out.
I don't want your stories. I don't want your
endings. It's too much work. It wears you out.
I just want Empty, Empty, Empty... Forever!

ALFRED

I should be careful what you say if I were you.
Your wish might very soon come true.

ANDY

What are you saying to me?

ALFRED

The stories I tell have to have an ending. Right
now I'm not quite sure what this one's going to be.
There are two possibilities. Either you get out of
here alive or...

ANDY

No! I want to change this channel.

Andy picks up the remote and pushes its buttons. On the TV
screen Hitchcock's image gradually begins to disappear,
leaving only a sinister Cheshire Cat smile.

Andy grabs the bell and begins shaking it. This time it does
ring as Alfred's image entirely fades from the screen.

130

ANDY

    Nurse! Nurse!

To his great relief the NURSE enters: an Irish nun in long
white robes, telling her rosary beads.

ANDY *(cont.)*

    O thank God. Nurse, I want a room with a phone.
    I want a better view. I want to see my friends!

It is only when the Nurse bends across him to smooth his
sheets and fluff up his pillow that he recognises her, beyond
her broad stage brogue. She gives a broad leering smile.

ALFRED *(as Nurse)*

    Now you know I can't let that riffraff in here.
    Didn't I just catch them in the pharmacy trying to
    steal the medication?

Andy realises that his Nurse is, of course, Hitchcock.

ANDY

    Oh no!

The caption comes up:

CAPTION

AD BREAK. PLACE SPONSOR'S MESSAGES HERE.

FADE TO BLACK.

7. INT. NOWHERE. ANY TIME.

Cutting between two formally posed interviews of Andy and
Alfred, separated from the story at hand, Alfred in his sober
if voluminous Savile Row suit and Andy, silver wig restored
with shades that reflect the image of the camera filming him.
Behind Warhol is a chroma-key image of his Cow Wallpaper.
Behind Hitchcock a menacing sequence from *The Birds* of the
crows massing on the children's climbing frame.

Softly under this:

VELVET UNDERGROUND SONG

    That's the story of my life
    That's the difference between wrong and right
    But Billy said both these words are dead
    That's the story of my life.

On Alfred:

                    ALFRED
When I was a child, of no more than six years old,
I committed a trivial act of domestic disobedience
that my father must have considered worthy of
reprimand...

                                            CUT TO:

On Andy:

                    ANDY
When I was a kid in Pittsburgh I used to get sick
all the time. My little eyes used to swell and
sometimes my hands would shake so bad my mother
used to have to feed me. The doctors told her
I had Saint Vitus Dance...

                                            CUT TO:

                    ALFRED
My father sent me down to the local police station
with a note...

                                            CUT TO:

                    ANDY
My mother gave me a Hershey bar every time I
filled a page in my colouring book.
I got to be real good at drawing...

                                            CUT TO:

                    ALFRED
When the sergeant on duty read this note he looked
extremely displeased. He took me down and shut me
in one of the cells...

                                            CUT TO:

                    ANDY
I found success in New York with a job drawing
shoe ads. But all the really cool people were
artists. So I had to figure out how to be an
artist. But I never knew what my paintings should
be about...

                                            CUT TO:

                    ALFRED
As the cell door slammed and the policeman turned
the key in the lock he looked at me and said:
'This is what we do to naughty little boys...'

                                        CUT TO:

                    ANDY
Then one of my friends said: 'What do you love
more than anything in the world?' I said 'That's
easy.' So he said 'OK, why don't you paint that...'

                                        CUT TO:

                    ALFRED
From that day forth I have gone to any lengths to
avoid arrest and confinement...

                                        CUT TO:

                    ANDY
That's why I started to paint money: five dollar
bills, ten dollar bills but mostly just regular
old George Washington U.S. Treasury one buck
greenbacks. And people started to buy them.
I guess they must have liked them a lot, they paid
more than a dollar...

                                        CUT TO:

                    ALFRED
Perhaps that explains why I've spent the best
years of my life making modest entertainments in
which innocent men, usually very slender, very
good-looking men, are on the run from an
implacable authority which believes them guilty...

                                        CUT TO:

                    ANDY
I couldn't paint them fast enough. That's why I
started with the silkscreens. Now nobody knows if
the pictures are mine or by somebody else. I think
that's so wonderful because they still pay anyway,
provided it's me who signs them...

                                        CUT TO:

                         ALFRED
    At least that's what my critics say. But I've
    told that story of my childhood so often that, to
    tell the truth, I really don't remember now
    whether it happened or not. I doubt my father
    would have ever perpetuated such a terrible
    trauma — he was a greengrocer.

                                            CUT TO:

                         ANDY
    And that's the story of my life in art...
    If that's what you want to believe.

                                            CUT TO:

8. PUPPET MASTER/HOSPITAL BED.

Hitchcock stands over a puppet theatre set of the hospital
room holding in his hand the strings which control an Andy
Warhol puppet.

                         ALFRED
    Bang, bang, bang. I've got him at my mercy...
                (imitating Mr. Punch)
    That's the way to do it...

He lets the figure fall onto the floor.

                                            CUT IN WITH:

Andy on his hospital bed:

                         ANDY
    I can't escape. I'll never get out of here.

                                            CUT BACK TO:

Alfred the Puppet Master looks at his toy now firmly placed
in the bed.

                         ALFRED
    He doesn't know whether he'll live or die. That's
    the way to do it.

                                            CUT IN:

Andy on the hospital bed:

                         ANDY
    Oh God, please don't let me die.

                                            CUT BACK TO:

                          134

Alfred looks down upon his creation.

> ALFRED
> But... it has to be said... I don't know either.
> And that's definitely not the way to do it...
> How am I going to get out of this one?

CUT BACK TO:

Andy's face on the pillow framed down through the crucifix.
(Reminiscent of the Dali *Crucifixion of St. John of the Cross*.)

> ANDY
> Oh God, if I ever get out of here... if You let me
> out of here, I promise I'll pray every day and go
> to Mass three times on Sundays... Oh gee, I
> already do. But don't tell my friends, they all
> think I sleep all day after Saturday nights
> parties. What can I promise? *(as if praying)* Oh
> God, if You let me get out of this, then I promise
> I won't curse, get high (except on diet pills and
> then only for work), I'll be extra kind to my
> mother and all the dumb animals and I'll never
> have relations with anyone: masculine or feminine,
> cute or ugly, above or below the age of consent,
> above or below the belt... Oh gee, I don't anyway.
> But please don't tell my friends, sometimes I
> think that spinning fantasies about my private
> life is the only thing they have to live for.

The angle changes so that once again Andy can see his face in
the TV screen, but this time it's just a pale reflection.

> ANDY
> What can I promise? All I ever wanted to be was a
> mirror. When a mirror looks into a mirror what's
> the reflection? Same again, right? That suits me
> fine. Let the Bs do all the work. I'll make the
> copies. I'll keep copyright... right? I'll just
> smile my enigmatic, Old Country, silk-screened
> Giaconda smile it took me from 1952 to 1957 to
> perfect — all that work every night in the mirror
> until my reflection disappeared. Let them talk
> while I make the running, while I keep the
> recorder running. Let the Bs make all the meaning.
> All I ever wanted to be was passive. Let the Bs
> project their stories onto me. Let the Bs make all

the honey. I'll be your mirror. That's why they
love me. Reflect what you are. Now all I can see
are the cracks. Something's got a hold of me and I
don't know what. No control anymore over my own
story. And it's painful. All I ever wanted to be
was a machine. Now I know I'm a body. And it hurts.

What am I going to do?   .

Suddenly the image of Hitchcock re-appears on TV screen.

                                        CUT TO:

9. TV SCREEN—TALKING HEADS.

Hitchcock is holding, crooked into his arm, a replica of his
own lugubrious face. (Like the famous pose with his model
head from Madame Tussauds.) Hitchcock is worried. But his
head is enjoying the predicament.

                    ALFRED
What am I going to do?

                    ALFRED TWO
Don't ask me. You got yourself in this pickle.

                    ALFRED
Five shots at point blank range and still the
bugger won't die.

                    ALFRED TWO
What about a who-dun-it?

                    ALFRED
I wouldn't stoop so low. Besides, everybody knows
who-dun-it: The murderer committed the cardinal
sin and confessed to the police before we went
on air.

                    ALFRED TWO
So you'll have to make a virtue of necessity.

                    ALFRED
What do you mean?

                    ALFRED TWO
Have him look out of the window.

                    ALFRED
Not that old chestnut.

                         ALFRED TWO
Very well then, what have got? a hospital room, a
man alone, his spirit hovers 'twixt this world and
the next. That'll give you some suspense.

                         ALFRED
Suspense? That's soap opera.

                         ALFRED TWO
Perhaps, in this case, soup opera. Our Sponsor,
for once, should be delighted. The Great American
Public on the edge of their sofas as they shiver
in wonder: Will he or won't he?

                         ALFRED
'Will he or won't he' what?

                         ALFRED TWO
Get out alive.

                         ALFRED
When all's said and done...

                         ALFRED TWO
You're a long way from that.

                         ALFRED
...Who really cares? It's only a movie, Alfred.

                         ALFRED TWO
Aren't we supposed to care?

                         ALFRED
I don't. Not any more.

                         ALFRED TWO
Don't be defeatist.

                         ALFRED
Alright then: let's start at the very end.

                         ALFRED TWO
A very good place to start.

                         ALFRED
Well?

                         ALFRED TWO
Well what?

                         ALFRED *(after a pause)*
Will he or won't he?

                              137

                    ALFRED TWO
That's what you're paid to invent.

                    ALFRED
It's a plausible enough beginning: man gets shot!

                    ALFRED TWO
Pull the other one.

                    ALFRED
I didn't know I had another one... till now.

                    ALFRED TWO
This is your job — you do this every week...

                    ALFRED
Intro. Then a word from Our Sponsor...

                    ALFRED TWO
Act One.

                    ALFRED
The Hook — get them watching.

                    ALFRED TWO
Then: Back after these messages.

                    ALFRED
Act Two: Get your hero up a tree.

                    ALFRED TWO
Another break. Sell more pet food.

                    ALFRED
Throw some rocks at him.

                    ALFRED TWO
Act Three:

                    ALFRED
Get him out of the tree. Just when they think they
know how it's going to end...

                    ALFRED TWO
The sting in the tale.

                    ALFRED
Chance'd be a fine thing.

                    ALFRED TWO
You've done it before.

                              ALFRED
          Ah... Let's just kill him off!

                                                  CUT TO:

10. INSERT. SHOWER ROOM.

Andy slips off a bathrobe, revealing his scars;
An eye watches him;
He steps into a white-tiled shower;
He looks upward;
Water shoots out of the shower head;
He bathes away his sins;
Suddenly the shadow of a bulky figure rushes in and raises a
carving knife...

An obvious but not slavish parallel of *Psycho*, culminating in
the terrifying Bernard Hermann score... which drains out
like the water in the shower, as:

                                              CUT BACK TO:

11. TALKING HEADS. AS BEFORE.

Alfred's head interrupts this fantasy:

                          ALFRED TWO
          No... I don't think so. We can't afford to kill
          him off.

                            ALFRED
          Why not?

                          ALFRED TWO
          Look what happened with *Sabotage*...
          Little Stevie gets a package to deliver by his
          evil guardian.

                            ALFRED
          Film cans. How appropriate.

                          ALFRED TWO
          We know it contains a bomb, set to go off at a
          quarter to two...

                            ALFRED
          'Don't forget: the birds will sing at one forty
          five...'

                          ALFRED TWO
          He leaves in good time, but...

                              139

                         ALFRED
         It's the day of the Lord Mayor's Show. London's
         chock a block.

                                                     CUT TO:

12. INSERT. *SABOTAGE* EXTRACT.

An extract from *Sabotage*, with the following dialogue more
precisely describing the accompanying images.

                         ALFRED TWO
         Will he or won't he?

                         ALFRED
         He gets on a bus, wedged in between two fat
         women...

                         ALFRED TWO
         Cut To:

                         ALFRED
         The clock at Charing Cross...

                         ALFRED TWO
         Cut To:

                         ALFRED
         Int. Bus. Day. Little Stevie pets a dog.

                         ALFRED TWO
         Cut To:

                         ALFRED
         The traffic lights change.

                         ALFRED TWO
         The hands of the clock move irrevocably towards
         the three quarter.

                         ALFRED
         Cut To: five different angles on the package.
         Cut To:

                                                  CUT BACK TO:

13. TALKING HEADS. AS BEFORE.

                         ALFRED TWO
         You blew up a bus full of innocent Cockneys!

                              ALFRED
          Nobody's innocent — especially not Cockneys.

                            ALFRED TWO
          You're no better than a terrorist.

                              ALFRED
          It was beautiful montage.

                            ALFRED TWO
          It was death by a thousand cuts. They walked out
          in droves.

                              ALFRED
          I'll be the first to admit I might have slipped up
          that time. He was a schoolboy, young and innocent.
          But this body's hardly the same, now is he? This
          body's a New York invert who hawks pictures of
          thirty-two varieties of soup cans that he doesn't
          even draw himself. They'll cheer to the rafters if
          he comes to a nasty end. It'll be a public service.

                            ALFRED TWO
          No can do, old man! How're you going to fill up
          the rest of the show?

                            , ALFRED
          Alright, so I redeem him, I let him live. What's
          he going to do: ride off into the sunset with
          Grace Kelly on his arm?

                                               CUT AWAY TO:

14. INSERT. *NORTH BY NORTHWEST*.

A flash extract from the very end of *North by Northwest* as
Cary Grant pulls Eva-Marie Saint into the top bunk of the
sleeping car next to him and the train enters the tunnel.

                                               CUT BACK TO:

15. TALKING HEADS. AS BEFORE.

                              ALFRED
          I hardly think it likely, somehow. He'll have to go.

                            ALFRED TWO
          It's your choice — you've made your bed. And he
          has to lie on it.

                                141

                              ALFRED
        What am I going to do? I've got nothing left to cut
        to. One more shot of that damned crucifix and I'll
        have the Catholic League of Decency down on me.

                           ALFRED TWO
        You wanted to do it on the cheap. You wanted to
        save money on the Costume and the Art Departments.

                              ALFRED
        Oh shut up. You're no help.

He throws the head like a football out of the set. When it
bounces off-screen he smiles as he hears a muffled: 'Ouch'.
The Caption comes up:

                             CAPTION
        INCREASINGLY PERSUASIVE WORDS FROM OUR SPONSOR.

                                                  FADE OUT:

16. INT. SOUND STAGE. DAY.

Fade up on Hitchcock standing on his sound stage, looking
around for inspiration. From the theatrical trunk he removes
a gun, a knife, a candlestick, a noose—Cluedo objects of
homicide, all tagged with exhibit numbers.

As he looks at them cut to his never changing expression.
Over this the Velvet Underground song:

                    VELVET UNDERGROUND SONG
        I'm sticking with you,
        'Cause I'm made out of glue.
        Anything you want to do
        I'm gonna do too...

Suddenly he is interrupted:

                         ANDY *(off-screen)*
        Hey...

He looks up.

                          ANDY *(o/s)*
        It's me... Maybe I can help you... Maybe I can
        make your movie for you.

                                                  CUT TO:

17. INT. HOSPITAL ROOM. AS BEFORE.

Andy lies on his bed as Hitchcock's face looks out of the TV set at him.

> ANDY
>
> Why not? I'd be quite happy to stay this way for the whole of the rest of the show. But it hurts me to see you looking so restless.

As he pushes one of the channel buttons on the remote his SPIRIT rises from the bed leaving his immobile body there and he is sucked into the set.

CUT TO:

18. INT. SOUND STAGE. AS BEFORE.

He emerges, wig intact, fully dressed, kneeling in profile at the side of Hitchcock. (As in the famous photograph of them together.)

> ALFRED
>
> Have you got a script?

> ANDY
>
> We don't need one.

> ALFRED
>
> We don't? What are you going to say?

> ANDY
>
> You're the star of this movie. The Superstar...

> ALFRED
>
> I said actors should be treated like cattle — not that they should resemble cattle. What am I going to say?

> ANDY
>
> Whatever you want.

> ALFRED
>
> There has to be a script.

> ANDY
>
> Reading other people's words sounds so phoney. A Superstar who can't make up his own lines can't be trusted to be real.

ALFRED

I can't do that. It's not my job.

ANDY

OK — we'll make a silent movie. No talk. No action.
Pure Cinema.

ALFRED

That's the way with us Catholics, even our cinema
has to be pure. What's the plot?

ANDY

There's no plot. Soon as you have a plot you have
to take on a moral position.

ALFRED

And that's God's job?

ANDY

No. It's just too hard to think up.

ALFRED

Something's got to happen.

ANDY

Something'll happen — we'll shoot a movie. That's
enough happening for one day.

They step out of frame...

CUT TO:

19. INT. FACTORY SET. DAY.

...and walk onto the Factory set where Andy was shot, finding
themselves in front of a large red couch. Silver cloud
pillows float in the air and silvered mannequins' legs jut
out of the ceiling. There is a 16mm movie camera set up
facing the couch and Andy goes over to it.

ANDY

OK, now take your clothes off.

ALFRED

Oh, so it's a dirty movie.

ANDY

That depends on the state of your BVDs.

ALFRED

I'm not going to be in any Underground movies.

ANDY

I've never been Underground. I never take the
subway and I want everybody to notice me. Now just
do what the director tells you.

Hitch begins taking off his clothes, eventually arriving at
a voluminous vest, blooming bloomers and suspenders holding
up his sagging socks.

ANDY

I'm going to call it *Suit*, or maybe *Andy Warhol's
Suit*, which will be kind of a joke as it's really
your suit and anyway we won't see any suit, just
you being measured for a suit. Maybe somebody'll
spot that and ask for their money back because
they paid to see a suit. Maybe I should put a pack
of cards on the couch, out of frame so if somebody
says: 'Where's the suit?' I can say there were
four suits... on the couch. Nah — nobody's going
to care.

ALFRED

What do I have to do?

ANDY

Just stand there.

A curly headed young MAN wielding a broom in the far corner
of the room comes over:

ANDY *(to the young man)*

Be a tailor, AOK?

ALFRED

He hasn't got a tape measure.

ANDY

He's not a method actor. Anyway, he's out of shot.
We only see from like here...

Andy draws an imaginary line just above Alfred's waist.

ALFRED

Then why did I have to get undressed?

ANDY

It has to be real.

ALFRED

You're just a voyeur.

145

                              ANDY
        How can you say that? As soon as I turn this on
        I'm going off to make a phone call. The only thing
        that'll be looking at you is the camera.

                             ALFRED
        It isn't even a real camera. Sixteen millimeter!

Andy turns on the machine and begins to walk off the set.
Hitchcock stops him as the other man begins to take
imaginary measurements.

                             ALFRED
         Wait!

                              ANDY
        Hey, we're rolling, don't look at me. Look at the
        camera.

                             ALFRED
        I can't look at the camera — they'll know it's a
        movie.

                              ANDY
        Of course they'll know it's a movie. It'll be
        playing at a movie theatre.

Now it is Hitchcock who feels naked and trapped.

                             ALFRED
        What am I supposed to do?

                              ANDY
         Whatever.

                             ALFRED
        Give me some direction.

                              ANDY
        Be yourself. I don't want to make you change for
        me. It wouldn't be fair.

He tries to set off again.

                             ALFRED
         Wait!

                              ANDY
        No point shouting, no-one's going to hear you.
        I told you it was a silent film.

                               146

                        ALFRED
    Tell me what to do!

                        ANDY
    Stop over-acting.

                        ALFRED
    I wasn't over-acting — I was blinking.

                        ANDY
    Just look blank. Oh gee, the film's run out
    already. I never got to make my phone call.

                                            FADE OUT.

20. INT. FACTORY. LATER.

Andy and Alfred sit on the couch in a blacked-out Factory,
behind them a projector beams *Suit* onto a white sheet tacked
up on the wall before them.

Cut between this and the projected movie played at silent
speed in which Hitch's face is noticeably more static and
spacey than he was on the set. The movie shows him framed to
the waist, occasionally a hand pops in and out, taking his
measurements. (Coloured filters are played upon the image like
the Eric Emerson sequence in *Chelsea Girls* — accompanied by
instrumental Velvet Underground feedback music.)

Sporadically over this:

                        ALFRED
    What am I going to do with this? This isn't a movie.

                        ANDY
    It's a slice of life.

                        ALFRED
    I'd rather have a slice of cake.

                        ANDY
    Umm, I just love cake.

                        ALFRED
    Nobody's going to want to watch this.

                        ANDY
    That's cool. Nobody's going to force them. I make
    movies that you don't have to go and see.

                          147

ALFRED

Nothing's happening.

ANDY

That's your problem. Don't you have anything else
to think about apart from what's going to happen
next? Watch what's there now.

ALFRED

It's boring.

ANDY

Only if you are. I make movies that give people a
chance to think about themselves for a change.
I made one movie about that lasted eight hours
about the Empire State building. Two hours in a
light went on. Everybody in the audience...

ALFRED

Everybody?

ANDY

...gasped. It was wonderful for people who didn't
have any place to sleep. I called the movie
'Empire' so everybody knew it was going to be a big
epic... like *Birth of a Nation*.

ALFRED

There's no suspense.

ANDY

Sure there is — you want to know when it's going
to finish.

Suddenly the film reaches the end of the spool. The punched-
out dots at the end of the roll of 16mm film puncture
Hitchcock's face then the image bleaches out altogether, the
end of the roll flaps loose and the room is lit by the
projector bulb.

ANDY

Oh wow. It's over. You want to watch it again?

ALFRED

No, please!

ANDY

What more do you want? You were just going to turn
there... then it ended. Who knows, something might
even have happened, if there'd have been more film

148

in the camera. But now we'll never know. Just like real life.

                    ALFRED
That's why I have no time for real life.

                    ANDY
Maybe I should call it *Andy Warhol's Thriller*.
At least you've got a film now.

                    ALFRED
This isn't going to sell any dog food. It's
wallpaper.

                    ANDY
I like wallpaper — it's democratic. Everybody has
wallpaper.

                    ALFRED
I don't think you've quite grasped it, have you?
We exist to keep people entertained. To stop them
walking out. To make them want to stay. To give
them something they don't have in their lives.
Some suspense. Watch!

                                        CUT TO:

21. SCREEN. FACTORY SET.

As Hitchcock talks, the events he describes can be seen on
the sheet on the Factory wall. It is the same space they are
sitting in complete with couch.

                    ALFRED *(off-screen)*
A man and a woman come into a room...

Alfred, wearing cricket flannels and a village club cap,
carrying a bat under his arm, walks into the room with Andy
who is dressed in high society drag with a blonde wig. It's
like a thirties drawing-room play. They sit down on the
couch and the conversation cuts between them.

                    ANDY *(on screen)*
Cocktail, precious?

                    ALFRED *(on screen)*
Do you have a radio, my dove?

                    ANDY *(on screen)*
I don't know that one, my angel. How do you mix it?

149

                    ALFRED *(on screen)*
The Test.

                    ANDY *(on screen)*
Well then, you've got me stumped.

                    ALFRED *(on screen)*
I was wondering whether Bradman had made his
century... at Lord's.

                    ANDY *(on screen)*
Why, has he gone to take the waters?

                    ALFRED *(on screen)*
Not Lourdes, my little Catholic.

                    ANDY *(on screen)*
My mother brought some holy water from the Grotto
in a cute little see-through vial in the shape of
the Blessed Virgin with a stopper in her head.
It makes you wonder...

                    ALFRED *(on screen)*
Does it, my little gold-digger? Wonder what?

                    ANDY *(on screen)*
What the Church used to do before they invented plastic.

                    ALFRED *(on screen)*
I never realised plastic was an ecclesiastical
contrivance, my swallow...

Over this, off-screen:

                    ALFRED *(off-screen)*
You see: fifteen seconds and the public are
already bored...

                    ANDY *(off-screen)*
I was just getting interested in her mother's
pilgrimage...

                    ALFRED *(off-screen)*
They're thinking: 'What's all this yap got to do
with the story... get a move on...' So...

Suddenly there is an almighty explosion. Off screen Andy
shrieks. When it clears there is only the ruins of the couch
left as the cricket cap and the blonde wig flutter to the floor.

                                        CUT TO:

                              150

Andy and Alfred on the couch, watching.

                ANDY
Gee, what a surprise.

                ALFRED
Precisely. Surprise is when they don't know what's
going to happen. Fifteen seconds of build-up and ten
seconds of shock. Just think how much it cost to do
that explosion and you've still got 89 minutes and
35 seconds left to think of. But what if...

                            CUT BACK TO:

Back on the screen: in very 'cutty' montage, accompanied by
thriller music an unidentified female drops a gun into a
paper sack of groceries, looks at a watch, then sets off.
Over this:

                ALFRED *(off-screen)*
Now we know something they don't.
Valerie Solanas, evil founder member...

                ANDY *(off-screen)*
...only member...

                ALFRED *(off-screen)*
...of SCUM, the Society for Cutting-Up Men, wants
to take her revenge on our lovely blonde heroine
for seducing her matinee idol husband...

                            CUT TO:

In the Factory Andy in drag is languidly pouring out two
glasses of Coke for himself and the still be-flannelled
Alfred. He spills some over his dress:

                ALFRED *(on screen)*
Oh what a dizzy dame you are, my little petal.

                ANDY *(on screen)*
That's why you love me, my sturdy stamen.

Andy steps behind a screen that splits the screen in two and
changes her dress in full view of the audience but
tantalisingly hidden from Hitch on the screen.

                ALFRED *(off-screen)*
Now we've got the Man on the Clapham Omnibus
interested — he might even stop resenting having
to pay for the tickets.

Back on screen: the titillation continues.

>   ANDY *(on-screen)*
> I guess plastic's brought us closer to the Source.
> It's very democratic... like Coke. A Coke is a
> Coke and no amount of money can get you a better
> Coke than the one that the bum on the corner is
> drinking. All the Cokes are the same and all the
> Cokes are good.

>   ALFRED *(off-screen)*
> You see? She can gabble on for ever about anything
> and he won't care — he's got something to look at.

>   ANDY *(off-screen)*
> So it's a dirty movie?

>   ALFRED *(off-screen)*
> Of course not — her undressing is entirely
> dramatically motivated.

>   ANDY *(on screen)*
> The President drinks Coke, Liz Taylor drinks Coke
> and, just think, you can drink Coke, too. All the
> Cokes are the same and all the Cokes are good...
> Liz Taylor knows it, the President knows it, and
> the bum on the corner knows it too...

She emerges from behind the screen in a robe and hands
Alfred a glass of Coke. He takes a drink and grimaces.

>   CUT TO:

Still on screen: Valerie Solanas, largely unseen, her face
hidden in shadow, closes the cage of the lift door and
begins, from many angles, her protracted but inevitable
journey upwards...

>   ALFRED *(off-screen)*
> So I've hooked him...

>   ANDY *(off-screen)*
> You talk about people as if they were fish.

>   ALFRED *(off-screen)*
> Quite. Let them fry! Now Little Miss Public's
> grabbing onto her Beau and thinking: 'Why all this
> talk of soft drinks? Don't you realise you're
> about to die! Do something — get her out of there!'
> And she wants the scene to stop, but really she's

enjoying knowing something that the characters in
the picture don't know... And the Big Bad Wolf...

>   ANDY *(off-screen)*
> The guy in the movie?

>   ALFRED *(off-screen)*
> No, her date in the picture house...

>   ANDY *(off-screen)*
> Right... I think.

>   ALFRED *(off-screen)*
> He's got his arm around his little shop girl
> closer than he'd dared on their first night out —
> perhaps he could even stick his hand under her
> dress and she wouldn't notice. And he's thinking:
> 'I'll come to one of this man's films again.
> He really knows how to drag out the agony.' So now
> I have a public mandate to keep this scene running
> for the next fifteen minutes. I've got them where
> I want them and only 75 minutes left to think up.

                                                CUT TO:

On screen: Back at cocktail hour in the Factory.
Cut In With the mounting elevator.

>   ANDY *(on screen)*
> In Europe the royalty and the aristocracy used to
> eat a lot better than the peasants... it was
> either partridge or porridge, and each class stuck
> to its own food. But when Queen Elizabeth came to
> the States and President Eisenhower bought her a
> hot dog I'm sure he felt confident that she
> couldn't have had delivered to Buckingham Palace a
> better hot dog than that one he bought for her for
> maybe twenty cents at the ballpark.

The assailant is all the while emerging from the elevator and
eventually entering the Factory space behind them so she is
still unseen by the characters on the screen.

>   ANDY *(on screen)*
> Not for a dollar, not for ten dollars, not for a
> hundred thousand dollars could she get a better
> hot dog. She could get one for twenty cents, same
> as everybody else.

> ALFRED *(off-screen)*

Watch out, she's behind you!

Alfred on-screen clocks the approaching danger.

> ANDY *(on screen)*

And that's why America is so wonderful, because the more equal something is, the more American it is.

A spaced-out Valerie comes up close behind him/her, her head down covered by hair:

> VALERIE *(on screen)*

Males are incapable of love... All the evils of the world emanate from the male incapacity for love... The only road to female liberation lies through the total elimination of the male species... Slave no more!

In an orgy of cinematic analytical editing cross-cutting of the action see: Valerie draw the gun; Andy's reaction; the whole action dragged out until the blonde Andy meets Valerie's gaze. As they look into each other's eyes he/she sees that Valerie is, indeed, played by Andy.

(It all gets a trifle complicated to explain round here but it's easy enough to imagine in the mind's eye... Isn't it?)

> ANDY *(on screen)*

No, Valerie, no... Not me...
(motioning Alfred) It's him you want...
Shoot him...

> VALERIE *(on screen)*

Eat this, cocksucker!

She fires; he falls; she fires again; his wig falls off; on screen Alfred gasps. It's just like a movie.

> CAPTION

EAT! DRINK! SMOKE! BUY!

> CUT BACK TO:

22. INT. FACTORY COUCH. DAY.

Back on the couch. Another Velvet Underground song.

> VELVET UNDERGROUND SONG

What costume shall the poor girl wear
To all tomorrow's parties?

ALFRED

That's why they call me the Master of Suspense.

ANDY

Why? Because you cut life around and speed life up
and slow life down and drag life out like you're
some kind of drug? I thought she was cute.
I wanted to hear her talk about Coke and hot dogs.
Surprise: she gets blown up. Suspense: she gets
shot. What's the difference? It still ends in
Death. Give her to me. I'll let her talk until the
film runs out. I won't have her die.

ALFRED

That's what they expect from me.

ANDY

Only because you made them expect that.
I think you enjoy being cruel.

ALFRED

You're the sadist — trying to make them sit
through your wallpaper.

ANDY

I give them a room. If they want they can stare at
the wallpaper.

ALFRED

They want to get out of their rooms. They want to
stop staring at the wallpaper.

ANDY

Who knows what they might see.

ALFRED

They'd see damp and dirt and mildew and mushrooms.
The poor buggers work hard — they deserve to be
taken out of themselves. They deserve some
excitement.

ANDY

Even if it's not their own?

ALFRED

Oh yes. Especially.

ANDY

At least in my work I never kill anybody.
My friends just kill themselves — when I'm not

looking, when the camera's turned off. I beg them
to call me when they're about to o.d. or jump out
of some window, so I can come visit and record.
But they never do. I guess I don't want them to...
not really. I'm happy with the bits in between.
The bits where they just be.

                    ALFRED
The public don't want your grotesque parade of
misfit friends dumped on them.

                    ANDY
You talk about the public like they're a toilet.

                    ALFRED
A convenience perhaps.

                    ANDY
Something you piss on.

                    ALFRED
They don't have to open their mouths. They can lie
in the gutter and look at the stars.

                    ANDY
Maybe if they learned to love the gutter they'd be
like my Superstars.

                    ALFRED
They're a bunch of drop-outs.

                    ANDY
Oh no. Don't you say that. Shame on you. Don't you
ever say that. The people in my movies are drop-
ins. If they don't drop in, they don't get to be
in the film.

                    ALFRED
You don't even pay them.

                    ANDY
I pick up their tabs at Max's. At least they make up
their own lines and stitch up their own gowns. That's
more than you can say about Tippi Hedren. They're
beautiful and I'm their Pope. My flock are
homosexuals, perverts of any kind, queers, thieves,
criminals of any sort, the rejected of society. Don't
they need to confess? Don't they need a Church?

                                        CUT TO:

23. EXTRACT: *I CONFESS*.

An extract from the beginning of Hitchcock's film, *I Confess*.
Quebec City; Hitchcock's cameo as he walks down a street;
direction arrows pointing to: A Dead Body! a figure in a
soutane leaves the murdered man's house; the guilty man
takes off the priest's garb as he walks down the street and
runs into a church. Inside, a Priest approaches the Murderer
who is now kneeling in the church: 'I must confess to you,
I must tell someone, I want to make a confession.' The
Priest goes into the confessional...

CUT TO:

24. INT. CONFESSIONAL SET. NIGHT.

A Confessional box in the corner of the sound stage.
Naturally, in the sanctum sanctorum the guilty party is
Alfred. Through the grille the Confessor is revealed as Andy.
(The scene has the tacky, flighty feel of one of Andy's
movies, like the Pope Ondine sequence from *Chelsea Girls*.)

                    ALFRED
        Forgive me, Father, for I have sinned.

                    ANDY
        When was your last confession, my son?

                    ALFRED
        Fifty years ago — when movies were still silent.

                    ANDY
        I hope it's more than thoughts and words. You got
        any deeds?

                    ALFRED
        Plenty.

                    ANDY
        Hm... what you got?

                    ALFRED
        Make yourself comfortable, Father. It's going to
        be a long night. Shall we start with murder?

                    ANDY
        How many?

                              ALFRED

I've lost count: I've killed them with guns, with
knives, with nail scissors, with neckties; in
black and white, in Technicolor, in 3-d. I've
shoved them off the roof of the British Museum,
Westminster Cathedral, Mount Rushmore and
the Statue of Liberty. I've done away with them in
foggy streets, in spotless motel bathrooms, in the
Royal Albert Hall and on the stage of the London
Palladium.

                               ANDY

What about sins of the flesh?

                              ALFRED

Oh yes! I undressed women — in public. I made them
stand in their scanties and subjected them to the
gaze of men with tape measures.

                               ANDY

These are terrible sins, my son.

                              ALFRED

It's not my fault. They made me do it!

                               ANDY

This is not a courtroom. I don't accept mitigation.

Close on Alfred:

                              ALFRED

It's true. For fifty years they put me on their
domestic payroll and my job was to take them out of
their mundane lives once a week. I was the
ferryman... they never begged me not to carry them
across the Styx. They wanted me to keep their
little minds occupied and I always did my best to
oblige. My father taught me: 'The customer is
always right.' I considered the stifling mundanity
of their lives and decided I would chauffeur them
to another world. Anything to be of service.
For I had discovered the chart to this other world,
running beneath the humdrum world they all lived in.

The surface of the road is thin as a shell, it's
waiting to crack. But they egged me on, you see.
For I had discovered that beneath the button-down
shirt of the Madison Avenue executive beats the

                               158

heart of a fugitive from justice. Behind the
spectacles and the twin set of the demure
secretary runs the hot blood of a rampaging minx.
Under the shiny white tiles of the motel bathroom
lies a fetid swamp. 'Please, walk this way.'
And they did.

This world of chaos and disorder is not of my
making. Don't blame the messenger for bringing the
bad news. I took them through the mirror and into
that world, but I never forced them to follow me.
And when they had seen what it was like down there,
I never forced them to make a return visit the
following week. How was I to know that they were
going to like it in the nether regions?
Don't blame the chauffeur for the view.

They wanted to look: through the curtains of the
opposite apartment; through the peep-hole in the
wall of my lady's chamber.

                    ANDY
If thine eye offend thee pluck it out.

                    ALFRED
Then who would look through the view-finder? They
wanted to play I Spy With My Little Eye. They kept
on blinking through their fingers when it got too
close to home, asking their partners to describe
what was happening as they hid under the cinema
seat or behind the settee in the parlour. They're
all dirty little keyhole peepers.

I told them not to look, really I did, but they
wouldn't listen to me: as they hung from the ledge
by their fingertips they couldn't resist that
fatal dizzying glance down onto the world they
once knew — fifty six stories below them.

They kept queuing up for more, honestly. I didn't
make them. In spite of my feeble protests they
begged me to lead them by the nose into my world.
And do you know why? Because it's the world where
stories come from. They might have been frightened,
but wasn't that anxiety alluring? Wasn't that
vertigo vertiginous?

Is it the pimp who creates the punter's need, even
if he is the one who walks away with the profit?
They came to me for a quick knee-trembler and now
you condemn me for taking a little pride in my
work. Guilt is the coin of the realm of our
species, Father. Guilt passes on like loose change
— it slides from the hand of the giver and drops
into the purse of the receiver. It belongs to
whomsoever may hold it. I'm just the honest broker.
Don't blame me for taking interest.

I think that's why they liked my stories. They
always felt quite at home with guilt.

They saw themselves in my heroes: good-looking
folk who weren't really guilty... but they might
as well have been. Just like it says in the Good
Book. Though they never did the deed they were
capable of the crime. What have I done that was so
terrible? I played a hunch that they all felt they
deserved to be punished.

I was never a tell-tale tit. Their guilty secrets
are safe with me. I showed you mine, but you never
showed me yours. My only sin was to throw an arc
light into the attic of my soul, and what a lot of
cobwebs that exposed. My only crime was to project
my nightmares onto a big white wall for everyone
to be privy to.

Back on Father Andy:

                    ANDY
This is what happens to naughty little boys.

But before he can deliver his penance:

                    ALFRED
Forgive me, Father, but there's one more sin I
have to commit... One more tale for the telling...
One more story that's not over yet...

Andy suddenly senses jeopardy — he turns and flees:

                                        CUT TO:

160

25. SHUFFTAN PROCESS SHOTS.

Andy finds himself in a series of classic Hitchcockian
jeopardies superimposed onto:
The confessional has become a telephone booth, bombarded
by birds;
He runs through the Dali drawings in *Spellbound*;
He runs through a gallery whose walls are covered with
Warhol-esque silk-screen portraits in elephantine scale of
none other than Hitchcock;
He falls spinning into the *Vertigo* maelstrom;
He lands in the mid-western field where there's a crop-
sprayer spraying where there ain't no crops and runs away
from its fire;
Finally, he sees before him a gigantic mountain sticking out
of the prairie into which is carved the colossal rock face
of Alfred Hitchcock.

CUT TO:

26. EXT. MOUNT HITCHMORE. DAY.

On Mount Hitchmore Andy climbs slowly, breathlessly, up the
granite nose of Alfred Hitchcock, negotiating the nostrils,
carefully seeking out hand and toe-holds. Just as he is
about to reach the cavity of the eye he slips and slides
down at accelerating speed a vertiginous vortex spinning
below him. But as he is about to be sucked into the abyss...
he reaches out and grabs hold of a single tuft of thick
foliage which forms a grotesque nasal hair.

He swings upon it to a safe landing on the pendulous lip.
But as he looks around he sees that waiting for him on the
ground is Hitchcock. Impossible to escape. He knows that it
is time to give in.

                    ALFRED
        Good evening!

                    ANDY
        OK, I guess you win.

                    ALFRED
        Not at all, I'm here to make you a little
        proposition. How much do you want to go back?

161

ANDY

To my brownstone on Lexington, with my mother and
the cats? Oh gee, Toto, there's no place like home.
Can I? Can I?

ALFRED

On one condition: If I let you out of here things
are going to be a little different.

ANDY

How so, different? I don't want it different.
I want the same for ever.

ALFRED

Then I'm afraid I'll have to let you go. Goodbye.

ANDY

Wait. Why does it have to be different?

ALFRED

Because it's the only way I can salvage the
semblance of a tale out of this mess. Don't you
see? You've been through Storyland, things have
happened to you. You looked Death in the eye.
You've had an adventure. You've been through a
rite of passage. You can't go into the refiner's
fire and expect to come out the same person you
were when you went in.

ANDY

Why not?

ALFRED

Because it's unsatisfying.

ANDY

Not to me, it isn't.

ALFRED

To the public.

ANDY

Not them again.

ALFRED

They expect their pound of flesh.

ANDY

They run you, don't they? You think it's you runs
them, but really they pull the strings.

ALFRED

What you've been through has made you realise that
you were never happy with what you were before.

ANDY

But I was.

ALFRED

This is not negotiable: the world you return to is
not the world you left.

ANDY

It was for Dorothy.

ALFRED

Nonsense. She left Kansas a girl and came back
from Oz a woman. What did you think was the
significance of the ruby slippers?

ANDY

A cute pair of shoes?

ALFRED

It was a symbol of her first menstruation.

ANDY

Ugh.

ALFRED

That's what French critics say.

ANDY

French critics say my work is a tongue in cheek
put-down of consumerism. I say: where else do they
expect me to put my tongue?

ALFRED

Believe me, I didn't want *The Wizard of Oz* either.
It's the best I can come up with. They'll feel
cheated if you learn nothing from all this hoo-hah.

ANDY

The only thing I've learned is not to trust you
and your stories. So what do I have to do? And
before you start, I am not buying any Kotex.

ALFRED

You have to turn your back on your old ways.

ANDY

What?

                    ALFRED

No more Superstars.

                    ANDY

No more Ondine? No more Rotten Rita? Ciao Sugar
Plum Fairy? Arrivederci Viva?

                    ALFRED

That's right.

                    ANDY

Then who am I going to play with? I have to have
Bs buzzing around.

                    ALFRED

You might try normal people.

                    ANDY

No more speed freaks?

                    ALFRED

I could perhaps allow drunks.

                    ANDY

I can't watch them shoot up and play on my
couch anymore?

                    ALFRED

I'm afraid not.

                    ANDY

Oh, it was such a lovely big couch. No more
flaming fairies?

                    ALFRED

We might tolerate the odd homosexual — provided
he's well-heeled.

                    ANDY

You mean I have to hang out with Ivy Leaguers, Wall
Street types in Brooks Brothers button down shirts?
Heteros whose wives don't understand them with big
booming laughs and last night's brandy on their
breath who'll crush my hands when we're introduced
and tell me that they just lurve my work?

                    ALFRED

The same. And preferably Nixon voters.

                    ANDY

No more drag queens?

ALFRED

Only heiresses.

ANDY

Then you have to introduce me to Princess Grace.

ALFRED

I might let you frug with her daughter Caroline.
Everybody else has.

ANDY *(starting to like this)*

Gee, Royalty! Queen Elizabeth?

ALFRED

Definitely no English Royals. Only those from
unpopular and/or repressive regimes. Perhaps I
could set you up with the Sharina of Iran.

ANDY

And maybe Imelda Marcos? I could paint her ruby
slippers... all three thousand pairs. *(starting to
have second thoughts)* But what am I going to do
with myself all day?

ALFRED

You're the first one who's ever asked me that.
Most of them are content I allowed them to get out
alive.

ANDY

Maybe I could go shopping.

ALFRED

Very well.

ANDY

I always liked to shop. My philosophy is that
buying's more American than thinking. But I still
have to do my work...

ALFRED

Confine yourself to society portraits.

ANDY

Business Art? OK, I could take Polaroid's in their
apartments so I can check out their furniture,
then silk-screen them and use one of the boys...

ALFRED

The *new* boys...

                              ANDY

     ... to give them a coat of paint and sell them for
     twenty five thousand dollars. I could do three a day.

                             ALFRED

     Capital. And no more films.

                              ANDY

     No more movies?

                             ALFRED

     Definitely not.

                              ANDY

     Oh gee, I don't know about that.

                             ALFRED

     Very well, it's your choice. Look!

He points off into the distance:

                                                     CUT TO:

27. INT. HOSPITAL SET. DAY.

Andy lies on his hospital bed seen as if through a distorted
fish-eye lens from the inside of the TV screen. Suddenly the
blip on the cardiac monitor stops pulsing and emits a high-
pitched whine. Close onto the bed. Gloved medical hands
appear to take the pulse, to pump the chest.

                    MEDICAL VOICES *(off-screen)*

     His heart's stopped beating...
     It's too late...
     We've lost him...
     Get him down to the morgue...

Andy and Alfred can be heard off-screen.

                    ALFRED *(off-screen)*

     Go back!

                      ANDY *(off-screen)*

     Uh-uh, I don't care anymore. I could get used to
     it out here.

                    ALFRED *(off-screen)*

     Please... the ending has to be 'up-beat'.

> ANDY *(off-screen)*

I am not a record. I am the hole in the middle of
the record. I am nothing. But without me nothing
can happen. I make nothing happen.

> ALFRED *(off-screen)*

Go back!

> CUT AWAY TO:

28. INSERT. POP ART.

Andy falls off Mount Hitchmore — a tiny speck finally falling
into a giant can of Campbell's Tomato Soup. (As on the
famous *Esquire* cover.) Then his soul is sucked back into the
prone body on the hospital bed.

> CUT BACK TO:

29. INT. HOSPITAL SET. AS BEFORE.

Back in the hospital room one of the Nurses takes a sharp
intake of breath. She notices that trickling down his cheek
is... a single tear drop.

> MEDICAL VOICES

Wait. He's crying! He didn't die! We saved him!
He's alive!

> CUT TO:

30. ABOVE AND BEYOND IT ALL.

Alfred and Andy are watching, looking down upon this
satisfyingly crass dénouement as if from on high.

> ALFRED

Alright, I admit it as corny as Kansas in August.
I'm far from proud.

> ANDY

No, that's so cute. Can't we just run out of film
on the teardrop?

> ALFRED

Goodbye, little Andy. You're alive!

ANDY

    Yeah. As soon as you stop wanting something,
    that's when you're going to get it. I've always
    found that absolutely axiomatic.

Before Hitchcock can leave Andy takes a Polaroid of Alfred.
A spectral ghost of a wraith-like impenetrable expression
plays across his face as the image on the photograph
gradually coagulates.

CUT BACK TO:

31. INT. HOSPITAL SET. AS BEFORE.

Back in the hospital bed Andy's eyelids movingly flutter,
then open:

ANDY

    We're am I? What happened to me?

The Caption comes up:

CAPTION

    BUY SPONSOR'S LIFE-GIVING PRODUCTS NOW!

CUT TO:

32. POLICE STATION SET. NIGHT.

Outside a monochromatic police station entrance a blue lamp
is burning. Alfred comes on in the comforting garb of a
1950's avuncular Dock Green policeman. His knees buckle as
he automatically checks his flies are fastened, coughs and
addresses us, increasingly demented:

ALFRED

    Good Evening all. Well the lad went straight, got
    in with a decent crowd and the last I heard his
    mother's very proud of him. Ah well, it's nice to
    know us coppers can sometimes do our bit, just so
    long as I don't have to have one of his pictures on
    my wall. Eight million stories in the Naked City
    and I had to pick his. My name's Friday. Today's
    Monday. Here comes Muffin, Muffin the Mule...

CUT TO:

33. INT. THE FACTORY. DAY.

Andy Warhol is making a Society Portrait from a Polaroid.
The silk-screen is squeegeed onto a canvas and Andy sloshes
on acrylic paint.

                    ALFRED *(v/o over this)*
        And they do say, on a moonlight night you can
        still hear the echo of Spring-Heeled Jack the
        Terror of London on the fog-drenched cobbles as
        the 'Eadless 'Orseman 'aunts these 'ills with 'is
        'ead tucked hunderneath 'is harm. Andy is saying
        'Goodbye, Goodbye.' Quick, Watson, into a hansom.
        The name, ma'am, is Simpson not Samson. Only the
        names have been changed to protect the ones with
        no names. Who knows what evil lurks in the hearts
        of men? Only the Shadow knows. And, friends, this
        story is true. I know, I was that soldier!

                                              CUT TO:

34. EMPTY SOUND STAGE. WHENEVER.

The *Alfred Hitchcock Presents* sound stage is empty now.
Hitchcock looks into the camera, in terror:

                    ALFRED
        Enough, please! Believe us, we can do it! How many
        times do you need us to tell it? It's easy when
        you know how. Why do you keep demanding it of me?
        Do It Yourself. Please! Please! End of Story!

                                              CUT TO:

35. INT. THE FACTORY. DAY.

The subject of Andy's Society Portrait is revealed to be:
a Famous Fat Film Director.

                    ANDY *(v/o)*
        'Who Done It? How Done It? Where Done It?' Who
        cares anymore? Why waste all that energy? One of
        these days, and it won't be long, even the
        President of the United States is going to be
        doing one of my Screen Tests and the whole world
        will be watching. Who cares: 'What do we know?
        What do we don't know?' The most powerful person
        in the world will be sitting there in front of a

shaky camera and a wobbly microphone drinking a
Diet Coke and telling everybody the intimate
details of his sex life in a voice you can't
hardly hear. And that's what they'll be watching.

                    ALFRED *(off-screen)*
        Impossible!

The Warhol portrait takes shape.

                                                    CUT TO:

36. INT. SOUND STAGE. AS BEFORE.

Hitch's composure is eventually regained. He turns to walk
away, his face blending into the distinctive caricature
profile of his TV show.

                    ALFRED
        Good Evening.

The music comes up: his theme tune, Gounod's *Funeral March of
a Marionette*, phasing into the chaos of *Sister Ray* by the
Velvet Underground.

                    THE END

Hitchcock caricature

THE GOOD HUMOUR CLUB.

The Good Humour Club was composed of tradesman and professional gentlemen of the city of York who met weekly throughout the middle of the eighteenth century to enjoy a hot dinner, to drink decent wine in moderation, and to promote the virtues of good companionship. Membership was limited to eighteen souls and one of the club ordinances stipulated that they must refer to each other as 'Doctor', if only for the duration of the colloquy. In 2013, through diligent scholarship, a momentous discovery was made which overturned previously held conventional wisdom in the field of

Laurence Sterne

Laurence Sterne Studies: the first volume of *The Life And Opinions of Tristram Shandy, Gentleman* was not, in fact, published in London in 1760—as printed on the title page—but rather the book must have made its first appearance in York at the end of the previous year! My friend from our youth, Patrick Wildgust, erstwhile thespian and book-dealer now the eminent and innovative custodian of Shandy Hall, Sterne's rectory in the Yorkshire parish of Coxwold, approached me to mark this milestone of literary detection with a drama. The first two volumes of this wonderful, entirely unique and utterly crazy, work were published anonymously... though there were certain 'clews' as to authorship which might well have been decipherable by a readership of his peers. We therefore decided that a meeting of the Good Humour Club on the day after publication would be an ideal setting for a play about the impact of *Tristram Shandy* upon its very first readers, before the work was made available in the metropolis and Sterne became the toast of literary London. The names and professions of the then current members of the Good Humour Club were known through surviving record books, but little or nothing was known of their characters or their reaction to Sterne's potentially scandalous volume. The drama was recorded in the appropriate surrounds of the York Medical Society Rooms on Stonegate.

*

DRAMATIS PERSONAE:

ELIZABETH SUNTON—Landlady of the Turk's Head Tavern, Stonegate and wife of Joseph Sunton, Victualler.

ISAAC NEWTON—Secretary of the Good Humour Club, profession unknown.

AMBROSE ETHERINGTON—Merchant Taylor of Stonegate.

HUGH ROBINSON—Merchant Freeman of the City of York.

JOSHUA OLDFIELD—Wine Merchant.

CHARLES ATKINSON—Surgeon.

ROBERT SMITHSON—profession unknown.

THOMAS SPOONER—Mercer and Woolen Draper of the Shambles.

THEOPHILUS GARANCIERE—Apothecary of Coney Street.

JOHN STORR—Watchmaker of Petergate.

REVEREND JOSEPH BRIDGES—Vicar of St Martin's, Coney Street, sub-chanter at York Minster.

JOHN HINXMAN—Bookseller at the Sign of the Bible, Stonegate.

The Good Humour Club © Martin Rowson, used by permission of the Laurence Sterne Trust, Shandy Hall

THOMAS CAUNTLEY—Silk Merchant and candidate for election as a member.

JONATHAN TASKER—Linen Draper and Silk Mercer of Coney Street.

*

INT. TURK'S HEAD TAVERN, HALLWAY AND STAIRS. EVENING.

NARRATION: *The Good Humour Club, at Sunton's Turk's Head Tavern, Stonegate in the City of York. Where are assembled the Worthy Members of this Honourable Fellowship on the evening of the Eighteenth day of the last month of the Year of Our Lord Seventeen and Fifty Nine.*

The clock strikes the hour: seven. Downstairs in the hallway of the Turk's Head the landlady, ELIZABETH SUNTON, fills the coal scuttle. A winter blast whistles as some of the MEMBERS enter, shaking the sleet from their coats before making their way upstairs to The Good Humour Club.

A Song to express the sentiments of the Company:

SONG: *In ev'ry walk of life his conduct scan,*
Good Humour, frank and honest marks the man.
Good neighbour, Good companion, Husband kind,
And to a servant's failings often blind.
Ne'er paying, by a sottish phrenzy led,
A broken bottle with a broken head.

INT. GOOD HUMOUR CLUB ROOM, UPSTAIRS. EVENING.

Under the song the Secretary, ISAAC NEWTON, is taking the Register in the Club Room:

NEWTON: Doctor Ambrose Etherington?

ETHERINGTON: Adsum.

NEWTON: Doctor Francis Bacon?

BACON: Adsum.

NEWTON: Doctor Hugh Robinson?

ROBINSON: Adsum.

NEWTON: Doctor Joshua Oldfield?

OLDFIELD: Adsum.

NEWTON: Doctor Charles Atkinson?

ATKINSON: Adsum.

173

The song is over now and the Register can be heard clearly:

NEWTON: Doctor Robert Smithson?

ROBERT SMITHSON *is not the brightest spark.*

SMITHSON: Adsum.

NEWTON: Doctor Thomas Spooner?

THOMAS SPOONER *is a wordly-wise man.*

SPOONER: Adsum.

NEWTON: Doctor Theophilus Garanciere?

THEOPHILUS GARANCIERE *is a crabby, self-important individual:*

GARANCIERE: Adsum.

NEWTON: Doctor John Storr?

GARANCIERE: Abest.

NEWTON: Yes, yes, Doctor Garanciere. We can all see he's
                   not here.

GARANCIERE: Mark him down for a fine next meeting.

But steps are coming up the stairs:

STORR: *(from outside)* Adsumming, Secretary.

JOHN STORR—*an open, pleasant individual—enters breathless.*

NEWTON: Doctor John Storr?

STORR: Adsum, Doctor Newton.

NEWTON: Reverend Doctor Joseph Bridges?

JOSEPH BRIDGES *is a dry, guarded, well-educated man of the cloth.*

BRIDGES: Present.

NEWTON: Reason for absence at the last meeting?

BRIDGES: No reason. No apologies.

NEWTON: Usual fine of sixpence to be levied.

BRIDGES: Surely, Secretary.

Coins are passed over and an entry made in the Minute Book.

NEWTON: Doctor Chas Ricard? Abest?

GARANCIERE: I sold him medication for a vicious head cold
                   only yesterday.

NEWTON:	Very well. Fines are not imposed for illness. Doctor John Hinxman?

JOHN HINXMAN *is urbane, superior.*

HINXMAN:	Present.
NEWTON:	Doctor Jonathan Tasker? *(looking around the room)* Not yet here I see.
HINXMAN:	I saw him this morning, Doctor Newton. He made a purchase from my bookshop.
GARANCIERE:	*(with some bitterness)* Aye… and not the only one.
HINXMAN:	He appeared in good enough health.
NEWTON:	I shall assume he is tardy and will be attending. Doctor Robert Barker?
GARANCIERE:	Abest absolutely.
NEWTON:	And with good cause, however. He has recently embarked upon the perilous venture of matrimony.
GARANCIERE:	No reason to prevent him being fined next meeting.
NEWTON:	Now, now. Our friend Barker has generously stood payment for a Crown Bowl of warming punch for the company.

Murmurs of appreciation all round.

NEWTON:	Doctor Chris Steele? Abest once again… Not attended for some weeks, has he?
GARANCIERE:	His membership should be suspended.
STORR:	Now wait on, sir. I have been entrusted with a message for the assembly. The dear old fellow begs leave to resign his place in this worthy congregation, on account of his great age and by reason of the streets not being properly illuminated…
SPOONER:	As the laws require…
NEWTON:	How true.
STORR:	Whereby on his last attendance he was put to great difficulty to find his way home.
NEWTON:	Duly noted.
STORR:	I do wish I had accompanied him.

NEWTON:	It's well known he lives further from this venue than many of the members.
STORR:	There is no necessity for him to give up his membership, surely?
NEWTON:	Perhaps there may be a precedent to be uncovered in the Minute Books for temporary suspension until the passing of this inclement winter weather.
STORR:	That would be a most sympathetic outcome, Secretary. It is particularly troublesome for someone with his infirmities to venture out of doors on bitter December nights.
SPOONER:	Especially one such as this when sleet is falling.
GARANCIERE:	Sleet? What are you calling sleet, Doctor Spooner? When I left my house it was most certainly snowing.
SPOONER:	*(ironic)* I hesitate to contradict a man of scientific erudition such as yourself, Doctor Garanciere… *(increasingly strident)* however, on my journey down Stonegate this evening I encountered not a single flake of snow.
GARANCIERE:	Humbug!
SPOONER:	Do you wish me to produce the evidence of my hat and good woollen coat… which were drenched by sleet!
GARANCIERE:	Snow!
SPOONER:	Sleet!

Storr attempts pacification:

STORR:	Might it not be, Doctors, that on the side of Coney Street Doctor Garanciere took from the Apothecary, what fell from the sky was indeed snow. Whereas on Spooner's route along the Shambles…
SPOONER:	*(interrupting)* No need to propose a meteorological prodigy to explain away this man's observational inaccuracy!
STORR:	I was merely suggesting a plausible escape from this unfortunate impasse.
GARANCIERE:	In the interests of exactitude, Secretary, I insist you record that on this night of December the Eighteenth it was, in the city of York, most definitely snowing.

SPOONER: For the sake of generations to come who may have cause to consult the history of this august gathering I advise you, Secretary, to write the weather down as sleet.

GARANCIERE: Snow!

SPOONER: Sleet!

Other members are taking sides. The Secretary attempts to maintain order.

NEWTON: Gentlemen! Gentlemen! Doctors all!

Bridges clears his throat and intervenes:

BRIDGES: Might we not settle this dispute by concurring that sleet and snow should be considered one and the same?

SPOONER: Certainly not!

GARANCIERE: Ridiculous!

BRIDGES: Ah, but what if I were to propose that snow is sleet... compacted; and that sleet is snow... liquifacted?

Approval from the members.

NEWTON: Well, Doctor Spooner?

SPOONER: I've no desire to debate the matter further, I grant you.

NEWTON: Doctor Garanciere?

GARANCIERE: With reluctance.

NEWTON: Splendid. Once again Good Humour prevails and the principles upon which this society was instituted have been upheld.

STORR: Might I propose a Standing Order—applying to the good Doctor Steele alone—which allows the agèd gentleman to attend whenever it may suit best him and that he shall incur no fine when absent?

SMITHSON: Seconded.

NEWTON: No dissension, I trust? Passed *nem con*. Now, it is my duty to convey news for those of you who may have not yet been privy to this sad intelligence concerning Doctor Tireman... Doctor Bridges, you are perhaps professionally more accustomed than myself to dispatching such tidings...

177

BRIDGES:	Certainly, Secretary Newton. Yesterday in the afternoon, after a sudden attack and but a few hours illness, Robert Tireman, a friendly sociable good-natured man and a worthy neighbour… *(a pause and a clearing of the throat—matter of fact)* dropped down dead.
NEWTON:	Is that so? In your capacity as a man of the cloth… might you not lead us in prayer, brother?
BRIDGES:	We commend his soul to whatever awaits… which we have no means of knowing. May his death offer a lesson of repentance to the surviving members of this Club. Amen.
COMPANY:	Amen.
NEWTON:	Which now leaves us with *two* vacant positions. The next item on the agenda is the introduction of a candidate for election as a new member to fill one of those posts. Step forward, Thomas Cauntley.

THOMAS CAUNTLEY *is rough-and-ready, somewhat vulgar.*

CAUNTLEY:	Present… Or should that be 'absum'?
GARANCIERE:	*Ad*sum!
NEWTON:	Your profession, sir?
CAUNTLEY:	Silk Merchant.
NEWTON:	A creditable calling.
CAUNTLEY:	It most certainly is.
NEWTON:	Do you swear before the company that you are a Freeman of this borough?
CAUNTLEY:	I do so absolutely, sir. Having recently arrived in York I very much wish to have my name set down on the club roll… I have been advised by those who should know that membership will do me no harm at all in advancing trade.
NEWTON:	*(with some distaste)* Mayhap. However, before you are allowed the privilege of induction it is incumbent upon me, Honourable Secretary Isaac Newton, to ensure you are conversant with the true purpose of The Good Humour Club and the composition of its worthy members.
CAUNTLEY:	Oh, yes indeed.

NEWTON: *(official)* Articles of Association of The Good Humour Club. One: Membership is composed of Freemen of the City of York. Two: Meetings take place weekly here at Sunton's house...

He is interrupted by the door opening and Missis Sunton entering noisily carrying the scuttle full of coals.

MISSIS SUNTON: I've brought your coals, Mister Newton.

NEWTON: Thank you, Missis Sunton. *(resumes)* Three: A forfeit of sixpence is payable for non-attendance...

He is interrupted again.

MISSIS SUNTON: What's your situation as regards candles?

NEWTON: Adequately supplied as ever, good lady. *(resuming again)* Four: The membership shall not exceed eighteen...

MISSIS SUNTON: It'll be me as'll be attending to you tonight, sirs, seeing as how Sunton hisself is down with an attack of the toothache. The apothecary can confirm the truth of that, seeing as I sent the girl out for witch hazel from you, did I not, Mister Garanciere?

GARANCIERE: Yes, yes.

MISSIS SUNTON: No effect in the slightest.

NEWTON: Then perhaps he should have the offending incisor removed. Do convey our regards for a speedy recovery, ma'am. *(another attempt at resumption)* Five: During the meetings all members shall address each other as 'Doctor'.

MISSIS SUNTON: *(interrupting)* Shall you be wishing to mix the punch yourself, Mister Newton?

NEWTON: I shall. *(another sally)* But the primary purpose of these gatherings...

MISSIS SUNTON: Then I shall put the kettle on the hob to boil.

She does so noisily. Newton is losing his patience:

NEWTON: ...The primary purpose of these gatherings is the promotion...

MISSIS SUNTON: I'll leave you gentlemen to your confabulations.

NEWTON: *(all patience lost)* ...the promotion at all times of Good Humour!

179

MISSIS SUNTON:	Don't hesitate to call me should further service be required.
NEWTON:	Thank you, Missis Sunton. *(recovering composure)* Excuse me, Doctors. And what precisely, we ask ourselves, is Good Humour?
CAUNTLEY:	Good living, good food and good drink.
NEWTON:	Why, indeed. But for us it is not a question of mere frivolous jocularity—though we strive always for an atmosphere of conviviality and merriment. Most of all Good Humour is a question of physical and mental balance.
GARANCIERE:	If I might provide a chemical definition for the edification of a potential new member, Secretary?
NEWTON:	*(wearily)* If you must.
GARANCIERE:	*(on his hobby horse)* The composing moistures of the human body have been recognised since the time of the Ancients as four in number: comprising Blood, Phlegm, Choler (otherwise yellow bile) and black bile (better known as Melancholy). These are the Humours. And should any one of them overly predominate in the circulation…
STORR:	*(cutting him off)* Speaking of circulation… Would you send that bottle round, Doctor Smithson?
SMITHSON:	With pleasure.
GARANCIERE:	*(pressing on)* …the temper of mind will be unnaturally affected, resulting in individuals characterised variously as: sanguine, phlegmatic, choleric or melancholic.
STORR:	As far as it concerns this man Good Humour signifies good company.

The Secretary regains control:

NEWTON:	What matters is maintaining a state of equilibrium, a state best achieved from passing over every trifle…
SPOONER:	Pass over the bottle, do!
NEWTON:	…By placing ourselves above all peevish follies and by upholding more real dignity…

Hard to do when Missis Sunton comes flouncing in again.

NEWTON:	*(cont.)* What is it now, mine hostess?
MISSIS SUNTON:	And here's me forgetting the ingredients for your warming winter punch bowl, following your preferred receipt as Sunton informs me: *(enumerating)* sugar… nutmeg… cinnamon… ginger… tea… a lemon ready juiced. Will you be preferring rum or brandy?
STORR:	Ah, both!
NEWTON:	Thank you, thank you. And, if I may prevail upon you, Missis Sunton, no more interruptions please. I am midway through the solemn induction of a new incumbent.

She leaves, put out:

MISSIS SUNTON:	Very sorry, I'm sure.
NEWTON:	…more real dignity than those who are the proudest— the vain and puffed up of this world. *(to the new applicant)* Thomas Cauntley…
GARANCIERE:	Perhaps the applicant here could demonstrate his commitment to our principles before we receive him.
CAUNTLEY:	How so, sir?
GARANCIERE:	Prove to us you subscribe to our purposes.
CAUNTLEY:	Oh, I do. I most surely do.
GARANCIERE:	More than mere assertion is required.
CAUNTLEY:	Well…
HINXMAN:	*(rescuing him)* You might share an example of wit and mirth.
CAUNTLEY:	Oh, I don't know.
HINXMAN:	Perhaps you might tell a jest.
CAUNTLEY:	*(after a thought)* Aye. Here's one I heard: A certain gentleman was prevailed upon to see a concert by a celebrated songstress whose shows had been the talk of York…
SPOONER:	Not Miss Kitty Fourmantel?
CAUNTLEY:	I mention no name of this nightingale.
SPOONER:	No… nor of the local prebendary who made such a fool of himself squiring Miss No Name around during the season.

181

Knowing laughter.

BRIDGES: I cannot possibly think to whom you might be referring.

SPOONER: Is that so, Doctor Bridges? I heard he was a friend and colleague of yours.

NEWTON: Pray continue.

CAUNTLEY: This gentleman secured a seat in the front row at the Assembly Rooms. And that evening Miss Four... *(stopping himself)* the singer in question was unfortunately partial to dining on onion soup with a consequent effect upon her breath. *(warming to the task)* When asked how he had enjoyed the recital the gentleman replied: 'The words were good, but the air was intolerable!'

The Company clap and cheer—even Garanciere joins in.

STORR: Bravo, Brother Cauntley.

NEWTON: All those in favour of admission?

'Ayes' from around the room.

NEWTON: Passed *nem con.*

GARANCIERE: A shilling must be levied for admission.

NEWTON: Thank you for the reminder. Indeed it must.

CAUNTLEY: I trust it will be coin well parted with.

Cauntley hands over his coin.

NEWTON: Then I declare: Welcome to the Good Humour Club, Doctor Cauntley.

COMPANY: Welcome, Doctor Cauntley.

THE CLOCK STRIKES THE QUARTER HOUR.

NEWTON: At this point in the proceedings it is customary to settle any wagers from the previous week's meeting. Doctor Hinxman?

HINXMAN: Secretary. You will recall last week Doctor Smithson remarked, somewhat incautiously it was generally considered, upon the increasing length and tedium of sermons in the Minster.

COMPANY: Indeed. Aye.

HINXMAN: When challenged Doctor Smithson wagered that Sunday's sermon was likely once again to exceed three quarters of an hour.

SMITHSON: *(sighing to himself)* Foolish of me!

NEWTON: Doctor Bridges, would you care to adjudicate.

BRIDGES: Certainly.

SMITHSON: What need? I'm well aware of the outcome.

BRIDGES: The sermon was preached by the Reverend Mister Sterne, incumbent of Sutton-on-the-Forest and Stillington in this diocese. His theme was *Job's Account of the Shortness and Troubles of Life considered.* He took as his text: *Man that is born of a woman is of few days and full of trouble. He cometh forth like a flower and is cut down. He flee-eth as a shadow and continueth not.* The Book of Job, Chapter Fourteen, Verses One and Two.

STORR: Melancholy incarnate!

BRIDGES: It was a most erudite, finely constructed, well-delivered and, I might add, *concise* address...

GARANCIERE: Aha!

BRIDGES: Lasting some few seconds under twenty-six minutes!

STORR: I timed it with one of my own watches—whose accuracy are known throughout the county—and it came in at twenty-six minutes and forty six seconds.

BRIDGES: That must be inclusive of both title and verse.

NEWTON: However it was calculated, the discourse fell several minutes short of Doctor Smithson's prediction.

GARANCIERE: You lose your bet, sir. The customary forfeit is to stand the company a bottle of port.

SMITHSON: Willingly—if my loss sets a precedent for shorter sermons!

Good Humour all round.

NEWTON: As tonight is the final meeting of this year—a week hence being Christmas Day—I feel notice should be made of much more important national events. This year can only be described as an *annus mirabilis.*

SPOONER:	As that fine parliamentary orator Walpole has been reported to state: 'Our bells are worn threadbare with ringing for victories'.
COMPANY:	Hear, hear!
NEWTON:	Yea, Seventeen Hundred and Fifty-Nine has indeed been a year of wonders for this great nation, the climax occurring on November the twentieth when Admiral Hawke defeated the French at Quiberon Bay, destroying so many ships of their fleet that any dastardly plan to infiltrate and invade Britain has been entirely obliterated.
COMPANY:	Shame! Damn them!
NEWTON:	Now every Englishman can sleep easily and the prospect for the New Year is one of complete optimism.
COMPANY:	Hear hear!
NEWTON:	I propose a toast to the Royal Navy!
COMPANY:	The Royal Navy!
NEWTON:	And to His Majesty King George the Second.
COMPANY:	His Majesty—God Bless Him.

At this point JONATHAN TASKER—*a most jovial fellow, not without wit—bursts in.*

NEWTON:	*(disapproving)* Good evening, Doctor Tasker.
TASKER:	Apologies, Secretary… Doctors.
GARANCIERE:	You're late. He must be fined!
TASKER:	I stopped to share a few pleasantries with our hostess. The clock was striking the first quarter as I came in the door of the house.
GARANCIERE:	Mayhap, but not the door of the clubroom.

Tasker is barely able to contain his enthusiasm:

TASKER:	There is a good reason for my tardiness.
GARANCIERE:	It had best be so, should you wheedle your way out of the penalty.
NEWTON:	*(reluctantly)* It's true you did miss the loyal toast, Doctor Tasker.
TASKER:	Very well. My sixpence. Take it and welcome.

Tasker hands over his coin and sits down breathlessly.

NEWTON: Gather your breath, Doctor Tasker.

STORR: Send round the cheering cup.

TASKER: Thank you.

As he drinks Tasker still cannot prevent himself from chuckling.

NEWTON: Do share with the company the reason for your mirth—so evident even before you've partaken the pleasure of our weekly fellowship.

TASKER: I am sorry, my friends. However, that's the very reason I did not arrive—for the first occasion on my reckoning—on time. I simply had to finish reading a certain amazing book. It's caused two tallow candles to burn out as I lost all track of the enemy. I was, quite literally, unable to put it down.

NEWTON: What could this extraordinary volume be?

TASKER: Extraordinary indeed. This morning I found trade at my silk emporium to be somewhat less than brisk—even considering the lateness of the year and the gathering clouds forewarning imminent possibility of snow…

SPOONER: Sleet!

NEWTON: That matter is long since settled! Pray, continue, Doctor Tasker.

TASKER: Yet I could not fail to notice a mass of mankind congregating outside the neighbouring bookstore.

STORR: The Sign of the Bible?

NEWTON: Your shop, Doctor Hinxman?

TASKER: Aye. But it wasn't the Good Book flying off your shelves, was it?

HINXMAN: Not today, no.

TASKER: Inquiring, from one of the gathering multitude, the cause of this unusual press of people, I was informed of a tome new-printed upon which the ink was barely dry and about which, I was assured, anyone who enjoyed diversion must certainly procure at all costs.

HINXMAN:	Best day of trading since I took over the management. More than half the stock sold on the first day of publication. Entirely unprecedented.
NEWTON:	*(somewhat left out)* I heard nothing of this literary phenomenon.
HINXMAN:	Your loss, Secretary.
NEWTON:	Do share with us: What volume could possibly have been the cause of such a bullish market?
HINXMAN:	Two miniature pocket volumes, in fact. Printed on superfine quality paper and retailing at the exceptionally reasonable price of five shillings the pair.
NEWTON:	Yes, yes. But what exactly is it?
TASKER:	This: *The Life and Opinions of Tristram Shandy—Gentleman.*

Tasker passes Volume One over to Newton who then sends it to greedy hands around the table.

NEWTON:	I see it bears the date Seventeen Sixty—somewhat premature as the New Year is yet a fortnight hence.
HINXMAN:	I expect that might be for the benefit of potential readership in the capital. The fashionable metropolitan crowd wouldn't wish to buy anything a year out of date, and one month is as obsolete as eleven.
NEWTON:	So it has been printed and put on sale here in York before London?
HINXMAN:	*(suddenly cagey)* That might be a speculation.
NEWTON:	What's this set of indecipherable letters?
CAUNTLEY:	Looks like Greek to me.
NEWTON:	This must be aimed at an educated market.
STORR:	*Your* enthusiasm, Doctor Tasker, therefore comes as something of a surprise.
TASKER:	I know no more of antiquated tongues than the man in the moon. But I didn't even peruse the title page, so eager was I to get my teeth into Chapter One.
SPOONER:	Doctor Bridges, you are a cleric and a university man...?

Bridges puts his spectacles on and phonetically transliterates, not without some difficulty, the Greek word by word:

BRIDGES:	*Terasi tis anthropos e ta pragmata alla tap eri tin pragmaton sog mata.*
NEWTON:	Yes?
STORR:	All Greek to me.
BRIDGES:	It translates as: *It is not things which trouble men, but opinions about things.*
STORR:	Some truth in that for sure.
BRIDGES:	The epigraph derives, I believe, from the Stoic philosopher Epictetus.
NEWTON:	You know, it might even serve as a motto for The Good Humour Club. I interpret this as an argument for balance in response to all things.
TASKER:	I would heartily commend this work to every member for the promotion of Good Humour.
GARANCIERE:	Harumph!
NEWTON:	It is clearly the product of an erudite pen.
TASKER:	True enough. Another part is written entirely in French untranslated.
GARANCIERE:	And so it should be given the subject it concerns.
NEWTON:	So you have read it too, Doctor Garanciere?
GARANCIERE:	I regret I was caught up in the general melée. I wish I had not expended my crown upon it.
TASKER:	But you did read it?
GARANCIERE:	In parts.
NEWTON:	Evidently including the part written in French. Why was a foreign tongue deemed necessary?
GARANCIERE:	On account of the topic under discussion.
NEWTON:	Which was?
GARANCIERE:	The topic under discussion was… *(in embarrassment, and with poor pronunciation)* 'baptême inter-uterine.'
STORR:	Eh?
GARANCIERE:	Inter-uterine baptism.
SPOONER:	I comprehend that to no greater degree when expressed in English.

187

GARANCIERE:	It refers to a distasteful Romish practice of baptising a child before it is born in instances when the mother's life is deemed to be in danger. In such circumstances, when the priest is unable to see any part of the unborn body, the rituals of the RCs allow the child to be baptised… *(embarrassed again)* '*par le moyen d'une petite canulle.*'
STORR:	And again I say: Eh?
GARANCIERE:	In English, to put it bluntly: A squirt.
STORR:	Ugh!
NEWTON:	So this a medical text?
GARANCIERE:	Certainly not.
NEWTON:	A theological tract, then?
TASKER:	Absolutely not.
NEWTON:	Written by a Roman Catholic? Or by someone who wishes to attack them?
HINXMAN:	You will notice that nowhere on the title-page is an author's name given.
NEWTON:	Then it is not the work of this gentleman 'Tristram Shandy?'

Storr bursts out laughing.

STORR:	Oh, I see!
SPOONER:	You're acquainted with the fellow, eh?
STORR:	Not at all. But I am well aware of 'shandy'.
NEWTON:	No need to be paradoxical, Doctor Storr. Do you know him or not?
STORR:	In the time-honoured vernacular of the rural portions of our county, as spoken by my dear parents, 'shandy' signifies 'crack-brained.'
TASKER:	Appropriate designation for this bizarre novel.
SPOONER:	Novel indeed.
NEWTON:	Then you too have read it, Doctor Spooner?
SPOONER:	I'm not one to be left out. It's the talk of the town.
NEWTON:	It is?

SPOONER:	But I cannot express the same degree of enthusiasm as my neighbour Doctor Tasker.
NEWTON:	Why so?
SPOONER:	I confess I found it hard to follow.
TASKER:	That's what intrigued me most.
SPOONER:	I continually failed to untangle the thread.
TASKER:	That's what gave me so much pleasure: Reading to be lost… then of a sudden coming across the map again.
STORR:	So it's a tale of travel? Of adventure?
CAUNTLEY:	Like Robinson Crusoe?
SMITHSON:	He came from York.
NEWTON:	He wasn't real.
CAUNTLEY:	*(disappointed)* Wasn't he?
SPOONER:	I could find not a single adventure in this volume.
NEWTON:	Is this 'Tristram Shandy' fellow real or fictional?
TASKER:	Now that is hard to say.
NEWTON:	How so? He can only be one or the other. No other logical possibility exists.
TASKER:	In point of fact… he barely exists at all.
NEWTON:	But the book purports to be the story of a man's life?
SPOONER:	Hardly. By the *finis* of the second volume the hero…
GARANCIERE:	If such he may be so designated…
SPOONER:	…hasn't even been born.
TASKER:	Implying further volumes are planned, Doctor Hinxman?
HINXMAN:	'Tis a consummation devoutly to be wished.
SPOONER:	*(chuckling)* The consummation… That part at least I could follow!
NEWTON:	Talk is for clarification, Doctor Spooner, not obfuscation!
SPOONER:	Pardon my hesitation… well, as there are no ladies present…
GARANCIERE:	Nevertheless, no need to overstep the conventional bounds of decency.

NEWTON:	I do wish you cabal would let the rest of us in on your secret.
STORR:	Yes, what is it all about?
SPOONER:	It's not exactly easy to characterise.
TASKER:	It's about… everything. And yet… nothing.
NEWTON:	*(exasperated)* Really!
GARANCIERE:	The purest lewdness from the very commencement.
CAUNTLEY:	*(intrigued)* Really?
TASKER:	*(laughing)* Oh yes! On the very first page, on the very first line, of the very first chapter…
SPOONER:	A chapter I had no difficulty in understanding.
TASKER:	…the story starts with the hero's parents in the midst of the act of his… *(searching for a euphemism)* geniture.
STORR:	Eh?
TASKER:	Conjunction.
NEWTON:	Do you mean there's a depiction of a scene of… ahem… copulation?
HINXMAN:	As I said: A consummation devoutly to be wished.
GARANCIERE:	Conception's no laughing matter.
SPOONER:	This one is. You see, before the father can effect a climax the mother interrupts him…
TASKER:	*In flagrante delicto…*
SPOONER:	And she breaks off to ask if he's not forgot to wind the clock.
STORR:	*(suddenly really engaged)* There's a clock in this story?
TASKER:	Certainly. Playing a most significant role.
STORR:	Then, for professional reasons alone, I shall surely have to obtain a copy. I shall visit your shop tomorrow, Doctor Hinxman.
HINXMAN:	Best be early.
GARANCIERE:	You can buy mine. I brought it here with me this night to petition Doctor Hinxman for a reimbursement of my five shillings wasted.

HINXMAN:	I am not a purveyor of used goods. Caveat Emptor.
GARANCIERE:	I shall accept four shillings and six.
STORR:	This edition of yours is somewhat well-thumbed.
SPOONER:	It appears you gave it more than a cursory perusal.
GARANCIERE:	Yes, I was reading it—before I threw the volume against the wall in disgust.
STORR:	I'm not buying battered goods.
HINXMAN:	I shall ensure two pristine volumes are reserved for you alone, Doctor Storr.
STORR:	Thank you.
GARANCIERE:	How do you justify peddling such filth?
BRIDGES:	*(sotto voce)* Apothecary, heal thyself!
HINXMAN:	I've shifted nearly two hundred copies today—almost more than half the print run. I fully expect to sell out tomorrow—on the second day of publication! It is already due to be reprinted and will be on sale in the metropolis by the beginning of the new year. As our fellow member Tasker confirms this is one of the most popular works I've ever offered for sale. Which leads me to wonder whether indecency might not emanate from the mind of the indecent.
STORR:	This clock... I don't suppose the author specifies the maker?
TASKER:	Far as I recall he only writes that it is a large house clock which requires winding once a week.
STORR:	I should have liked to know.
SMITHSON:	I doubt if it were one of yours, Doctor Storr.
STORR:	Pity. Though the merest mention of a clock is of interest to me. Perhaps I can skip the less savoury passages.
GARANCIERE:	*(sceptical)* Oh yes?
SPOONER:	Doubtful. And why excise the choicest bits?
TASKER:	Such moments are but a small part of the whole.
NEWTON:	It yet remains for you to reveal the nature of this whole.

TASKER:	Impossible without telling everything. All I can say is that whoever wrote it is extremely fond of digressions and exceptionally adept at giving his Readers the slip— to my great amusement.
NEWTON:	Is it memoir? Or invention? Is it a work of history? Or of imagination? Is it fact? Or is it fiction? Is it philosophic? Or is it humorous?
TASKER:	All of these… And yet none.
NEWTON:	*(even more exasperated)* Well, what is it? Is it satire?
TASKER:	If so then the target of the lampoon must be every last one of us poor specimens of humanity; the way we act; the way we think; the way we are; the way we imagine ourselves to be.
GARANCIERE:	Bah!

THE CLOCK STRIKES THE HALF HOUR.

HINXMAN:	There was a recent trend in the trade for works of satire. That vogue has gone out of fashion.
GARANCIERE:	Hear, hear to that.
SPOONER:	The last satirical squib I recall was published here in York but a few months since.
NEWTON:	What was that?
SPOONER:	Don't you recall the hoo-ha over *A Political Romance*?
NEWTON:	Ah yes.
STORR:	That tract about an old watch-coat and a pair of black plush breeches?
SMITHSON:	What's that?
STORR:	It was a tale of a parish officer who takes for his own use a good warm watch-coat which should rightly be for the benefit of the church sexton.
NEWTON:	On the surface, maybe. But sharper intellects prepared to dig deeper would discern it is clearly an allegory about recent disturbances on the continent of Europe.
SPOONER:	The machinations of the King of Prussia in particular, to my way of thinking.
SMITHSON:	Whereas I supposed it to concern the Partition Treaty of Italy, surely.

SPOONER:	What the deuce has Italy to do in the affair? It was clearly Germany.
NEWTON:	Italy, eh? I had not considered that interpretation. Your explanation has too much ingenuity in it to be altogether slighted.
GARANCIERE:	And too much to be credited. Whatever this squib might have been allegorising of, thankfully all unsold copies were ordered to be destroyed by the Archbishop himself before it could achieve wider circulation.
HINXMAN:	Suggesting to me it rather concerned matters closer to home… ecclesiastical scandals the knowledge of which His Grace was keen to suppress. *(knowingly)* Eh, Doctor Bridges?
BRIDGES:	There was some such speculation.
STORR:	I never did understand why it caused such offence to the Archbishop.
HINXMAN:	We need not look to Italy or Germany for the key to unlock that conundrum.
GARANCIERE:	All I know is that blasted tract took a swipe at the remedies of my profession—for which calumny alone it deserved to be consigned to the flames.
STORR:	Nothing whets the spirits like an insult!
HINXMAN:	The sharpest intellects of all were able to see this for what is was. Could not the portrayal of a greedy, pimping petty-fogging parish officer be a representation of a certain Commissary and Keeper-General of the Exchequer and Prerogative Court of York? And, if so, the honourable Sexton who opposes his self-serving machinations could be none other than our Dean.
BRIDGES:	Careful, Doctor Hinxman!
HINXMAN:	Small wonder the Archbishop felt his nose tugged and dirty linen laundered before the eyes of the world by this fine-spun satire and so intervened in such a despotic manner to suppress the free expression of opinion.
STORR:	So that's what all the fuss was about!
BRIDGES:	One interpretation amongst many.

HINXMAN:	One which overthrows every other far-fetched supposition, and establishes the certainty of mine own beyond the possibility of a doubt. That should be the last word in the debate.
NEWTON:	So it wasn't about Italy?
GARANCIERE:	*(a growing suspicion)* Hold hard, sirs. We all know the progenitor of that devilish satirical stroke designed to foment dissension amongst the townsfolk, don't we?
SMITHSON:	We do… Do we?
SPOONER:	Aye. The very same preacher of that what-do-ye-call-it which cost you a bottle of fortified wine this evening: The Reverend Mister Sterne.
TASKER:	The Vicar of Sutton and Stillington.
NEWTON:	Your friend Laurence Sterne.
BRIDGES:	It's no secret Lorry and I have been companions and colleagues since we were both scholars at the university—he at Jesus, myself at John's… which is more than can be said for any other members of this fraternity.
TASKER:	The hero of Tristram Shandy declares he too was a student of Jesus College.
BRIDGES:	Now there is a coincidence.
GARANCIERE:	It cannot be denied the style of that pamphlet did betray a certain supercilious similarity with that of these volumes which, for some unaccountable reason, have caused Doctor Tasker such mirth… a clever-dickery, a smug tom-foolery.
TASKER:	You have a point, Doctor Garanciere, it can't be gainsaid… however crabbily expressed. At one stage in the story…
GARANCIERE:	Do not persist in dubbing this eccentricity a story.
TASKER:	The narrative comes to a definite halt…
GARANCIERE:	Narrative? Halt? It never takes off. Like the London mail-coach I once caught which remained mired in mud outside Grantham.
TASKER:	*(persisting)* And one of the characters…

GARANCIERE:	More wooden puppets jerked around on visible strings than 'characters'.
TASKER:	To whit Corporal Trim, the servant of Tristram's father…
STORR:	Wasn't the sexton in that political romance also called Trim?
NEWTON:	Hmm!
TASKER:	This Trim discovers a sermon by Yorick…
STORR:	The Shakespearean clown?
SPOONER:	No! The rural parson!
TASKER:	Trim delivers this sermon in full. The theme is *The Abuses of Conscience*. And I was sure I had read it before.
GARANCIERE:	To include a sermon in a smutty tale is nothing short of blasphemy!
BRIDGES:	On the contrary. It might be thought such an introduction would raise the moral tone of any volume.
GARANCIERE:	Or it might be the greatest outrage against sense and decency that has been offered since the first establishment of Christianity.
BRIDGES:	Passing, of course, over the persecutions of the Emperor Nero, the martyrdom of the Protestant faithful, the tortures of the Spanish Inquisition…
GARANCIERE:	If this inclusion is designed to be uplifting how come it is delivered by a comic manservant and one of the listeners drops off to sleep?

The penny is beginning to drop.

TASKER:	You sold *A Political Romance,* didn't you Doctor Hinxman.
HINXMAN:	Very few copies. The work could find hardly any readers. A box would still remain gathering dust in my storeroom were it not for the Archbishop's injunction to put the tracts on the bonfire.
NEWTON:	Did you publish it?
HINXMAN:	Certainly not. It was, if I recall, entirely paid for by the writer himself.

SPOONER:	Come to think of it, I too recognised a familiarity. I'm sure I heard this sermon preached some years since. Do you remember *The Abuses of Conscience*, Doctor Bridges?
BRIDGES:	*(reluctantly)* Ye-es. It was given as the annual Assize Sermon in the Minster about a decade ago.
STORR:	Preached by a certain prebendary, before a thousand witnesses, ready to give oath of it.
SPOONER:	And printed by him for subsequent sale.
NEWTON:	And who was the divine in question?
BRIDGES:	I'll not dissemble, gentleman. That too was the work of the Reverend Mister Sterne.
TASKER:	So Sterne is Yorick?
SPOONER:	And Yorick is Sterne?
TASKER:	Ergo, Sterne must be the author of *The Life And Opinions of Tristram Shandy, Gentleman*.
NEWTON:	Well, Doctor Hinxman?
HINXMAN:	The condition of publication requires me to preserve the anonymity of the author.
NEWTON:	Well, Doctor Bridges?
BRIDGES:	The condition of amity requires me to preserve my silence on this matter.
NEWTON:	Even among we Good Humourists?
BRIDGES:	How long do you think the mystery would remain within these four walls?
GARANCIERE:	So that's your opinion of your fellows.
NEWTON:	Surely you must have been vouchsafed the identity of the writer, Doctor Hinxman.
HINXMAN:	I am a bookseller merely. Printed commodities arrive in my shop and I do my level best to make sure they leave. In this instance I am pleased to say, they are leaving with prodigious alacrity.
NEWTON:	I hear neither of you denying it is by Sterne.
TASKER:	Good Parson Sterne—the Yorkshire Yorick. I'll raise a glass to him for one.

BRIDGES:	I am certainly not confirming this man—who like myself is a humble and unworthy labourer in the clerical vineyard—to be the author.
SPOONER:	Well, if it really is by him he'll no longer have to preach in the Minster for one pound per pop.
NEWTON:	I propose we mobilise and examine what has already been put before us in somewhat of a forensic manner…
HINXMAN:	Should we not respect the author's wish to remain in the shadows?
SPOONER:	Over and above our desire for knowledge? Never!
NEWTON:	Let us together sift the evidence scientifically and soberly in peace and harmony.
CAUNTLEY:	Pass the bottle peacefully, Doctor Smithson.
SMITHSON:	Harmoniously, Doctor Cauntley.
STORR:	This is as notable and curious a disputation as ever was engendered in the womb of speculation.
NEWTON:	What clews thus far point to the identity of the author?
TASKER:	Consider the Yorkshire connection…
NEWTON:	There is one?
TASKER:	The book is put on sale this very day in York and nowhere else as yet. I submit that, therefore, the book must have been printed here.
NEWTON:	Doctor Hinxman?
HINXMAN:	An unproven hypothesis.
NEWTON:	But not an unreasonable one?
HINXMAN:	Possibly not.
TASKER:	Work of such quality can be produced by only one printing house within these city walls: That of your late predecessor in the office of Club Secretary, Doctor Newton.
NEWTON:	Caesar Ward, rest his soul.
TASKER:	And now managed by his widow.
NEWTON:	Did Ann Ward supply you with your copies, Doctor Hinxman?

HINXMAN:	That I can surely verify. Ward's is without doubt the finest printing house in the county.
SPOONER:	If it is printed in York and sold in York then the writer must likely be from York.
HINXMAN:	More vain speculation.
TASKER:	Not at all! This is confirmed in the book itself!
SPOONER:	How so?
TASKER:	The action…
GARANCIERE:	Or total lack thereof.
TASKER:	The action of the tale is indubitably set in Yorkshire.
SPOONER:	From my perusal—incomplete and intermittently uncomprehending I'll be the first to concur—the location is surely never specified.
TASKER:	Not explicitly.
SPOONER:	The actual name of the county is even at one point disguised by a discreet dash.
TASKER:	Ah, but remember the chapter concerning the Shandy family's own dash from London to fulfil the father's desire that the child be born in his own country house—in spite of the not unreasonable objections of the expecting mother?
SPOONER:	Oh yes. A quaint conceit!
TASKER:	From details of the journey north I am strongly of the opinion that it must be inferred that Shandy Hall can be located nowhere but in our own county. This is without doubt the work of a native resident.
NEWTON:	We've already discussed the inclusion of the sermon…
STORR:	Endless is the search of Truth!
TASKER:	Which was incontrovertibly written, delivered and subsequently published by the Reverend Mister Sterne.
BRIDGES:	But which might, of course, have been included as a quotation—an homage to an undoubtedly skilled practitioner of the art of the pulpit.
STORR:	Why would any author put forward at such length any other man's prose but his own?

TASKER:	Parson Yorick is described as a victim of clerical conspiracy and lack of preferment.
STORR:	Not unlike the Vicar of Sutton and Stillington himself.
GARANCIERE:	Well deserved, no doubt.
TASKER:	The writer observes of Yorick... if I can find the passage: 'They had smote his root, and then he fell, as many a worthy man had fallen before him.'
GARANCIERE:	If he's courting sympathy he'll get none from me.
SPOONER:	Then we have the 'coincidence' of the two characters nominated 'Trim'.
TASKER:	And the perceived and certain similarity of style between this work and Sterne's earlier effusion this year in his *Political Romance*.
NEWTON:	Might not the raucous reception and fiery treatment of that controversial piece provide an explanation as to why the author chooses in this instance to hide his identity?
SPOONER:	Particularly given the amusingly indelicate contents.
TASKER:	The epigraph is in Greek...
SPOONER:	Betokening a classical education...
TASKER:	Yet the work is quite approachable by the unlearned English reader.
STORR:	Something to be thankful for. I *will* buy a copy, Doctor Hinxman.
NEWTON:	In spite of passages written in Greek and French?
SPOONER:	Surely it must have been penned by a university man?
STORR:	Such as Sterne.
TASKER:	A scholar of Jesus College, Cambridge?
STORR:	Such as Sterne.
SPOONER:	A clerk in holy orders?
STORR:	Such as Sterne.
GARANCIERE:	A clergyman's pen should be dedicated to the production of sermons and morally uplifting tracts with a secure scriptural foundation.

NEWTON:	All roads lead to Mister Sterne.
TASKER:	Well, Doctor Hinxman?
SPOONER:	Well, Doctor Bridges?
GARANCIERE:	Should it transpire that this minor prebendary is the concealed identity under discussion then my estimation of the man tumbles yet further than it has been heretofore. For he must have been engaged in the production of this humbuggery at the very time sore afflictions were visited upon his poor wife.
NEWTON:	You know the good lady?
GARANCIERE:	Very few are fortunate enough to escape crossing the threshold of an apothecary's emporium.
SPOONER:	Missis Sterne was your patient?
GARANCIERE:	As has been near everybody around this table.
NEWTON:	What was her terrible infirmity?
GARANCIERE:	Truly, Secretary, delicacy forbids…
SPOONER:	Sounds as if you're speaking of a female malady.
GARANCIERE:	Oh no. I can say with total certainty the visitation of such a condition takes no account of gender.
STORR:	Come now, no secrets among fellow inductees.
GARANCIERE:	It seems to me as if this entire evening thus far has been beset by secrecy.
NEWTON:	Not for much longer, if I have any say in the matter.
TASKER:	Well, Doctor Hinxman?
HINXMAN:	I assert I am merely the vendor.
SPOONER:	Well, Doctor Bridges?
BRIDGES:	I assert I have not been a reader.
NEWTON:	Pray reveal whatsoever you are privy to, Doctor Garanciere!
GARANCIERE:	*(embarrassed)* It was, in fact… emerods.
STORR:	What-are-odds?
CAUNTLEY:	The grapes of wrath.
STORR:	Eh?

CAUNTLEY: Piles.

NEWTON: Is that so?

GARANCIERE: A perfectly natural occurrence.

SPOONER: As is childbirth, as depicted in *Tristram Shandy*.

GARANCIERE: But not something to be made an object of amusement, rather a medical condition to be written about by none other than medical authorities for the enlightenment of their fellow medical professionals.

BRIDGES: *(under his breath)* Preferably in Latin.

CAUNTLEY: Arse fruit.

SPOONER: Your coyness does you no credit, Apothecary. Are not what we plain-speaking folk call 'piles' openly mentioned in Scripture?

NEWTON: Is this so, Reverend Doctor?

BRIDGES: Indeed it is—as recounted in the first book of Samuel. When the Philistines take away the sacred Ark of the Covenant and sacrilegiously install it in the temple of Dogon, their fish-headed idol, the Lord of Hosts smites both young and old with... and I quote from memory: *'emerods in their secret parts... and the cry went up to heaven'.*

STORR: I've no doubt of it.

TASKER: What I heard is that the lady went raving mad.

STORR: It surprises me not a jot that such small swellings could produce such a monstrous effect.

TASKER: Rumour had it she came to imagine herself The Queen of Bohemia necessitating confinement in the house of a Lunatick Doctor.

SMITHSON: That would have given her husband some peace and quiet.

NEWTON: So your prescriptions served scant solution.

GARANCIERE: It was not a result of the emerods, believe me. Diseases of the brain are beyond my capabilities. I may know the cause... but I know not the cure.

THE CLOCK STRIKES THE THREE QUARTER.

NEWTON: Then what else could have been the cause of such peculiar behaviour?

GARANCIERE:	Word is Elizabeth Sterne caught her husband in bed with the maid.
BRIDGES:	Calumny! Vile rumour and hearsay! Take it back, sir!
GARANCIERE:	It was on good authority from one of his parishioners.
BRIDGES:	The wife's misfortune cannot in any manner be attributed to the husband's behaviour.
GARANCIERE:	So you dispute that, on account of him, she was shut up in a madhouse?
BRIDGES:	For a short while only, due to a stroke of the palsy, which could be the lot of any unfortunate creature. I am happy to report the dear soul has made a complete recovery and is living in Mint Yard.
SPOONER:	Where she must have become aware of her husband openly cavorting with the delightful Miss Fourmantel.
CAUNTLEY:	The talk of York.
GARANCIERE:	A divine should at all times exercise Prudence.
SPOONER:	In the case of this divine it was Kitty being exercised!
BRIDGES:	If my worthy friend found solace in squiring this songstress…
GARANCIERE:	Young enough to be his daughter…
BRIDGES:	It was to surely fill an uncomfortable gap in the poor man's heart. It is not good for man to be alone.
GARANCIERE:	It is contrary to the seventh commandment to commit adultery.
BRIDGES:	Companionship should not be mistaken for concupiscence.
NEWTON:	But such open, foolish courtship was, for a man of the cloth known throughout the diocese, in the very least somewhat incautious.
GARANCIERE:	Scandalous I'd call it.
BRIDGES:	I have my friend's word there was never any impropriety committed.
NEWTON:	Sterne's conduct became a subject of widespread speculation, however it might be characterised.
BRIDGES:	Such idle gossip should be beneath men of good heart such as ourselves.

SPOONER:	I have every sympathy with the man's philandering. *(shudders)* I too have crossed paths with the wife… in a professional capacity.
GARANCIERE:	Missis Sterne has many virtues.
SPOONER:	Aye, but they stand like quills upon the fretful porcupine, ready to go forth in sharp arrows on the least supposed offence.
GARANCIERE:	I have never known her to have done a wrong thing.
SPOONER:	Aye, but she does right things in a very unpleasing manner.
GARANCIERE:	In my estimation she is a woman of great integrity.
SPOONER:	In my experience the only way to avoid a quarrel with her is to keep a due distance. My opinion is as diametrically opposite to yours as East is from West.
NEWTON:	Perhaps she has more respect for her apothecary than for her woollen draper.
SPOONER:	I'll allow the fellow his Kitty with full understanding.
GARANCIERE:	Libertine!
TASKER:	Now there again… Another mirror held up to life. In the book there's reference to a shadowy beauty with whom our first-person narrator is heartily enamoured but with whom he denies any wrong-doing.
SPOONER:	'Dear Jenny?'
TASKER:	Indeed. Let me find the passage… Ah, here I have it— indulge me for a moment *(reading)*: *'Not that I can be so vain or unreasonable as to desire you should think that my dear, dear Jenny is my kept mistress. No, that would be flattering my character in the extreme and giving it an air of freedom, which, perhaps, it has no kind of right to. All I contend is that you, or the most penetrating spirit upon earth, should know how this matter really stands. Is there anything unnatural or extravagant in the supposition that my dear, dear Jenny may be my friend? Surely a friendship between the two sexes may subsist, and be supported without anything but that tender and delicious sentiment which ever mixes in friendship, where there is a difference of sex. Let me intreat you to study the pure and sentimental parts of the best French Romances. It will really astonish you to see with what a variety of chaste expressions*

this delicious sentiment, which I have the honour to speak of, is dressed out.'

GARANCIERE:	Methinks the villain doth protest too much.
TASKER:	I contend that Shandy's Jenny is none other than Sterne's Kitty.
CAUNTLEY:	Was she also partial to dining on onion soup?
NEWTON:	The road stops at Sterne.
TASKER:	Well, Doctor Hinxman?
NEWTON:	Admit it! The writer of *A Political Romance* and *Tristram Shandy* are one and the same.
HINXMAN:	I do concur the evidence is mounting.
SPOONER:	Well, Doctor Bridges?
NEWTON:	Admit it! Parson Yorick is Laurence Sterne in disguise.
BRIDGES:	Those are your words.
NEWTON:	Which you can gainsay no longer.
HINXMAN:	Well, Doctor Bridges?
BRIDGES:	Well, Doctor Hinxman?

A collective gasp at the revelation—simultaneously:

HINXMAN:	Behold the man.
BRIDGES:	Ecce Homo.
GARANCIERE:	At last some much-sought transparency among peers. Devil take him.
TASKER:	So this child can be laid at his door, Lord bless him.
GARANCIERE:	Let us devoutly desire that when this intelligence is spread around there'll be kindling for another blaze.
BRIDGES:	I implore you—and all of you around this table—not to expose this secret until the writer chooses to reveal himself openly.
SPOONER:	Fond hope. The word will be carried on the winter winds through the precincts of the Minster by this p.m. tomorrow.
BRIDGES:	Please, I beg you to protect my friend.

NEWTON:	It does you no credit to accuse these honest fellows, your companions. There must be others outside this circle privy to the solution of this riddle.
GARANCIERE:	It won't be merely the bonfire this time. When the Archbishop casts his eye over this filth it'll be Sterne's living up in flames.
BRIDGES:	Nonsense. His Grace will find nothing to displease him as an ecclesiastic and much to amuse him as a man.
GARANCIERE:	If so, 'twill be on account of the weeks and months the Archbishop dallies in London, corrupted by metropolitan dissipation. He should spend more time in his diocese, breathing the clean air of Yorkshire.
NEWTON:	Your robust defence, Doctor Bridges, is not solely for the man but for his work. You *have* read this book, despite your assertion to this company you had not!
GARANCIERE:	It is contrary to the ninth commandment to bear false witness. You treated the members of this club to an untruth, Rector!
NEWTON:	Retract, I insist! That's not a word allowed within this room. However, there does appear to have been dissemblement afoot.
BRIDGES:	On my honour, not at all.
GARANCIERE:	You swore you had not read it.
BRIDGES:	Ah, but I did not say that portions had not been *read to me*—along with a select few.
GARANCIERE:	You university men—slipperier than Jesuits.
STORR:	Best retract that too. Even worse an insult to a good Anglican.
NEWTON:	And you too were in on the game, Doctor Hinxman?
GARANCIERE:	Another... 'dissembler' in our midst.
HINXMAN:	I never explicitly denied to you my knowledge of the book or its author.
NEWTON:	Not in so many words.
SPOONER:	You must have had dealings with him prior to publication?

HINXMAN:	I prevailed upon him to excise local references. I determined this too significant a publication to be dismissed as a provincial work.
NEWTON:	Are you intimating we are a provincial readership?
HINXMAN:	A descriptive term, Secretary. No qualitative affront implied.
GARANCIERE:	But one inferred, Master Bookseller. This is not the first occasion I have evinced your superior demeanour. I believe it is your flaunting desire to quit this place and peddle your wares in Saint Paul's churchyard in the city of London rather than Stonegate in the city of York.
HINXMAN:	I merely considered the protection of anonymity to be the wisest course. I counselled caution and prudence.
GARANCIERE:	While you were filling your purse at—of all places—the Sign of the Bible.
HINXMAN:	That was the name conferred upon the business by my predecessor.
GARANCIERE:	Then perhaps you should change it should you wish to persist in the publication of indecency.
SMITHSON:	I wager the good Reverend will reveal himself before we meet again in the New Year. The lure of celebrity will be far too strong.
STORR:	I'll take your wager, Doctor Smithson.
GARANCIERE:	If his nonsense catches on in London the circumference of his noggin will swell to a size even greater than his wife's piles.
HINXMAN:	I predict great fame.
NEWTON:	And great sales.
TASKER:	Was the book read to you by its author, Doctor Bridges?
BRIDGES:	Indeed it was.
TASKER:	How I truly wish I could have been part of that assembly. To hear the words from the horse's mouth.
CAUNTLEY:	From the ass's arse.
TASKER:	Did it occasion you as much diversion as it did myself?
BRIDGES:	Eminently so. I believe *Tristram Shandy* will prove uniquely innovative in the annals of literature.

GARANCIERE:	Unique in the catalogues of smut.

BRIDGES: It is ingenious; droll; poignant; sensible; pathetic; entertaining and above all, from a moral perspective, profitable.

GARANCIERE: Immodest; tedious; mean; witless; nonsensical and above all, a vile obscenity. His character as a clergyman is entirely impeached by printing such gross and vulgar tales as no decent mind can endure without extreme disgust!

NEWTON: It does seem passing strange that a work of such controversy—liable, as is witnessed here, to be the cause of just offence—should emanate from the pen of a clergyman?

BRIDGES: On the contrary. There are several such literary precedents.

NEWTON: There are? You do surprise me.

BRIDGES: Consider the great François Rabelais for one.

GARANCIERE: A popish monk... and French to boot.

BRIDGES: And Jonathan Swift—Dean of Saint Patrick's Cathedral in Dublin.

NEWTON: Another papist?

GARANCIERE: And Irish to boot.

BRIDGES: An Anglican like ourselves... which did not prevent him from displaying a prodigious sense of outrageous humour.

GARANCIERE: Then he, too, should shrink in shame, as I shudder in disgust at the state of England's clergy.

NEWTON: The only question which should concern us now is: Does *Tristram Shandy* promote Good Humour?

BRIDGES: Gentlemen, within these city walls malicious tittle-tattle provides a constant source of entertainment and amusement for minds unfurnished with more exalted ideas. Within the Minster surrounds feuds and factions constantly bubble and burst, splitting asunder men whose vocation should cause them to be brothers as they are caught in these webs of discord. What does such gossip, what do such disputes signify in the great order of life? Not a mote.

Do you imagine God looks down upon mankind, His creation, through the firmament from the heights of the seventh heaven and throws in his lot with one party against another? Our Lord's commandment is that we should love our neighbours as ourselves. Granted this is an all but impossible injunction—especially in the company of the ignorant—but its very difficulty is signification of its ultimate importance. And given that we are exhorted to be kind to one another, does that not also imply we must not be too hard upon ourselves? The Golden Rule is to love others *as ourselves*. And what can more promote mutual kindness one among the other than the provocation of laughter? Does not laughter ameliorate the distress occasioned to all in this vale of tears? And is not the alleviation of the troubles of our fellows the duty of every true Anglican? Is not, therefore, a writer who interprets his mission to inspire honest mirth…

GARANCIERE: Immoderate mirth!

BRIDGES: …not, thereby, fulfilling his Christian mission to the utmost? And is not the hilarity thus provoked the best of all remedies? Maintaining the balance both of our inner physical constituents and our outer spiritual aspirations?

GARANCIERE: Bawdiness is un-English and indecency can never constitute Good Humour. I go further: bawdiness is blasphemy.

TASKER: I doubt I shall ever witness a more pertinent demonstration of the wisdom and truth of this book, whose writer so justifiably proclaims: *'When a man gives himself up to the government of a ruling passion, or, in other words, when his Hobby-Horse grows headstrong, farewell cool reason and fair discretion!'*

GARANCIERE: It's you, sir, who are mounted upon a Hobby-Horse… on the road to Hell.

SPOONER: As long as a man rides his Hobby-Horse peaceably and quietly along the King's highway without compelling anyone else to get up behind him, pray, what have the rest of us to do with it?

The colloquy is becoming increasingly heated and personal.

TASKER:	What qualifies you as a critic, Garanciere? A book is not so easily constructed in the same manner as your mountebank concoctions of pills and potions.
GARANCIERE:	Proof indeed, if any were needed, that these unruly, impertinent volumes lead to only one destination: the destabilising of the brain and the inflammation of the passions.
CAUNTLEY:	That's two for a start.
TASKER:	Anyone with the wit to put prejudice aside when turning these pages must feel as I did that another one of my fellow creatures had allowed me privileged entrance to his most profound and innermost thoughts.
GARANCIERE:	Impertinent, eccentric fancies.
TASKER:	Anyone understanding enough to open his head and heart to such access must experience, as I experienced, such a shock of recognition which cannot help but lead inevitably towards the profound realisation that this mind runs along tracks remarkably similar to our own.
BRIDGES:	Hear, hear!
GARANCIERE:	Then you must be as unbalanced as its progenitor.
TASKER:	It is you who have lost your balance. True Shandeism, if I may call it thus, opens the heart and lungs, and forces the blood and other vital fluids of the body to run freely through its channels to make the wheel of life run long and cheerfully round.
GARANCIERE:	Seek not to lecture one versed in the art of a subject of which I am the only professor in this company. Your words are far silkier than any of the merchandise you higgle. Your brain is swimming and about to drown.
TASKER:	On the contrary it is you who are out of equilibrium, sir. You are neither sanguine nor phlegmatic and I do very much detect an excess of the choleric combined with the melancholic.

Garanciere leaps across the table and begins to scuffle with Tasker.

SMITHSON:	A half guinea on Tasker.
STORR:	I'll take your wager.

As the Others attempt variously to separate them or urge them on, Newton tries with no degree of success to restore order.

NEWTON: Of all the positive virtues of the mind, I do not know of any more desirable than Good Humour. No quality renders the possessor more easy and happy in himself or recommends him more forcibly to other people…

TASKER: Take your hands off me!

NEWTON: *(persisting)* There is no situation in life, no engagement in business, no party of pleasure, wherein Good Humour will not contribute to mitigate disappointments or heighten enjoyment.

GARANCIERE: You would try the patience of a Job!

NEWTON: *(struggling)* And whether we are partners for life, or partners in a country-dance; whether we are associates in great and mighty undertakings, or companions in a post-chaise, we should, on every occasion, cherish and keep alive this agreeable disposition…

TASKER: There never was any thing to be won in wrestling with a Chimney-Sweeper—all you get is soot-smeared.

NEWTON: *(floundering)* We should be the more attentive to encourage and preserve this pleasing quality of Good Humour, because it has been observed that many people lose it by little and little in the progress of their lives. Life is like a game at backgammon. If an unlucky throw comes, we must make the best of it, and play on without grumbling at our ill luck…

Garnciere is bashing Tasker with the book.

GARANCIERE: This is all your dashable book is good for.

STORR: I'd say I'll be taking your money, Doctor Smithson.

SMITHSON: Not for the first time has Dame Fortune deserted me, Doctor Storr.

Newton attempts to shout above the increasing racket:

NEWTON: But who would venture to sit down to the table with a man who could not bear an adverse cast without turning over the board in a fury, and throwing the dice-box at his companion?

The clubroom door opens and Missis Sunton appears, shocked. Silence prevails.

MISSIS SUNTON:	Gentlemen, please! What has occasioned so much disturbance amongst you?
NEWTON:	A book, ma'am.
MISSIS SUNTON:	Not another disputable political tract to cause such intolerable anguish?
NEWTON:	*(sheepish)* A story book.
MISSIS SUNTON:	A silly story book? I would have thought you to be above such trifles. I don't hold with reading, especially these new-mangled novels: the infatuation of idle snuff-taking chambermaids neglecting their honest labour to waste candle power.
NEWTON:	Please accept the apologies of all of us.
MISSIS SUNTON:	I do hope all this turmoil has not made you dyspeptic. The House has prepared an elegant supper.
SPOONER:	Far from it, Missis Sunton. Nothing like a heated debate to assist the flow of stomach juices.
MISSIS SUNTON:	Then I'll bid the girl to bring in the goose with potatoes and greens. *(bellowing out)* Betsy!!! As it's Christmas this spread is compliments of the house.

Cheers and 'thank yous' and rhythmic clapping as the dinner is brought in.

NEWTON:	Brava, Good Lady!
MISSIS SUNTON:	There's hot apple pudding and custard to follow.
NEWTON:	Splendid!
MISSIS SUNTON:	Sunton sends his apologies but his jaw is still terrible inflamed notwithstanding the frequent application of witch hazel until the phial was exhausted, but he does not wish to inflict upon you gentlemen his prodigious pain.
NEWTON:	Thanks and commiserations to Our Host.
COMPANY:	Hear, hear!
MISSIS SUNTON:	Therefore would you allow me have the honour of carving for you in his place?
NEWTON:	Thank you for your solicitous offer but this pleasant duty should best defer to the Club Secretary.
MISSIS SUNTON:	Then I'll leave you gentleman to your repast. Merry Christmas.

COMPANY:	Merry Christmas.

She leaves.

NEWTON:	Reverend Doctor Bridges, would you lead us in the Grace?
BRIDGES:	Dear Lord, Thou knowest it is Thy will that the consumption of products, as well as the manufacturing of them, gives bread to the hungry, circulates trade, brings in money, and supports the value of our lands. Therefore we give Thee thanks that by the exercise of our appetites we may give spur to our nation's economy. Amen.
COMPANY:	Amen.
NEWTON:	Good Humour is once again restored.

THE CLOCK STRIKES THE HOUR: EIGHT.

THE GOOD HUMOUR CLUB—THE END… UNLESS IT IS WISHED THERE MIGHT BE AN EPILOGUE?

Perhaps the last word might be given to the voice of THE AUTHOR?

AUTHOR:	Could a historiographer drive on his history, as a muleteer drives on his mule—straight forward, for instance, from Rome all the way to Loretto, without ever once turning his head aside, either to the right hand or to the left—he might venture to foretell you to an hour when he should get to his journey's end. But the thing is, morally speaking, impossible. For, if he is a man of the least spirit, he will have fifty deviations from a straight line to make with this or that party as he goes along, which he can no ways avoid. He will have views and prospects to himself perpetually soliciting his eye, which he can no more help standing still to look at than he can fly. He will moreover have various: Accounts to reconcile; Anecdotes to pick up; Inscriptions to make out; Stories to weave in; Traditions to sift; Personages to call upon; Panegyricks to paste up at this door; Pasquinades at that. All which both the man and his mule are quite exempt from. In short there is no end of it. I am resolved not to be in a hurry; but to go on leisurely…

THE END.

THE

L I F E

AND

O P I N I O N S

OF

TRISTRAM SHANDY,

GENTLEMAN.

Ταρασσει τὰς Ἀνθρώπυς ἐ τὰ Πράγματα,
αλλα τὰ περι τῶν Πραγμάτων, Δογματα.

VOL. I.

1760.

Title Page of the first edition of The Life and Opinions of Tristram Shandy, Gentleman

FRAGMENTS—WHEN SIGMUND FREUD DID NOT MEET FLINDERS PETRIE.

The exhibition *Freud & Egypt* was a collaboration in autumn 2019 between two London museums: the Freud Museum in Maresfield Gardens, West Hampstead, where Freud and his family lived in the last months of his life after fleeing Vienna, and the Petrie Museum of Egyptology, one of London's hidden gems secreted in an alley off Gower Street, housing the most amazing collection of ancient Egyptian artefacts. Freud—the 'father of psychoanalysis'—was a passionate, indeed obsessive, collector of antiquities and the exhibition, curated

Freud At His Desk by Max Pollak. Used by permission of the Freud Museum, London

by Professor Miriam Leonard, included objects from his collection which had been smuggled out of Austria, together with others unearthed by Flinders Petrie—'the father of scientific archaeology', who was also, by the way, a passionate, indeed obsessive, proponent of eugenics. Ivan Ward, Deputy Director of the Freud Museum, was my fellow student of Social Anthropology at King's College, Cambridge back in the dear, dead days beyond recall and he asked if I might be interested in writing something for a conference in connection with the exhibition. My response was to imagine an encounter between these two 'fathers'.

As they had never met 'in real life' this dialogue would have to be imaginary and it would also, given Petrie's racial views and resistance to self-examination, have to be somewhat spiky. What might possibly connect them apart from the objects on display? Petrie had conducted the first excavation at Tell el Amarna, site of Akhetaten, city of Akhenaten, who tried to impose a monotheistic religion upon his people. And this 'heretical pharaoh' plays a central role in one of Freud's last works 'Moses and Monotheism', partly written during his exile in England, in which he proposes a controversial hypothesis about the origins of Judaism.

The performance took place in both museums with Giles Croft, former Artistic Director of the Nottingham Playhouse, playing Freud—at least he has a beard—and myself personating Petrie—without attempting his apparently reedy, piping voice.

*

INT. STUDY, MARESFIELD GARDENS. DAY.

An ageing, bearded man stands in his study carefully unwrapping a collection of small ancient statuary and arranging them on his desk in an order known only to himself, stroking some of them as if they are his favourite pets. This is SIGMUND FREUD.

FREUD: Released... My collection! All my old grubby gods; my
           faithful friends; the remaining members of my family.
           Reunited. All my Egyptians.

           Ptah: the architect, creator of the world by thought alone.
           Mut: how could it be that the ancients came to choose the
           vulture as the symbol of motherhood?
           Thoth: who weighs the hearts of the departed... how soon?
           Osiris: the promise of immortality.
           And the Sphinx... ah, the riddle of the Sphinx.

           From Vienna to London, from Berggasse to Maresfield
           Gardens. They have made the journey—as we have
           journeyed. Smuggled out from under the noses of the

215

authorities—as we have been smuggled out. Exiled—as we are exiled.

All have arrived in safety. Not a single object damaged, not one of them confiscated, and with only a minimal levy extorted. How can I ever thank my loyal friend, Doktor von Demel, curator of the Kunsthistoriches Museum, for deliberately underestimating their value so they might be packed and dispatched from Austria? Judged worthless by the Reich. Priceless to me. Such a great feeling of security to know they will be on my desk, at the last, where I will live… and die… in freedom, here in magnanimous England.

A niggling voice with scornful English intonations, at first barely audible to Freud, interrupts him. Whose is it? Where does it come from? From inside himself? Surely not.

VOICE: A collector… bane of my life.

FREUD: *(disturbed)* I cannot deny I am a collector. And I may say at once that I am no connoisseur, simply a layman…

VOICE: An amateur… laying out his trinkets, stripped of all original context, for his personal gratification.

FREUD: *(perturbed)* I am no hoarder. Do not imagine I am like some miserable old bachelor compulsively counting his assortment of snuff boxes.

VOICE: A dilettante… polishing his treasure trove in his private museum.

FREUD: *(protesting)* I am no miser. I never sought the most fashionable objects… Though, despite my much-vaunted frugality, I suppose I have sacrificed a great deal for my collection. But I always paid low prices for some prized possession offered by Robert Lustig, my dealer at his antique shop on Wipplinger Strasse.

VOICE: Dealers… the tomb-raiders of our day.

FREUD: True enough, I am possessed of the questing spirit—I could never pass any emporium with a sign beckoning 'Antiquities'.

VOICE: Unscrupulous profiteers fuelling the greed of those who dig merely for spoil.

FREUD: *(protesting too much?)* Why should I deny these ancient works of art have been a source of exceptional recreation and unsurpassed comfort? But I have never engaged in some

216

childishly impossible pursuit, some anally retentive quest for completion. And I have never taken food from my own children's mouths to satisfy an urge to collect. No, the desire to possess has never possessed me. In fact, I have always taken great delight in giving away my finds as gifts to those in my circle… sometimes even to my patients. For me, collecting has never been an addiction.

VOICE: I have often… no, sometimes… well, only very occasionally… had cause to wonder what possible pleasure could be derived to people such as yourself from the ownership of articles such as these.

FREUD: I feel no great need to analyse my needs. Why should an explorer of the psyche feel compelled to scrutinise every last one of his *own* impulses? Tobacco was my only addiction… *(not without regret)* I wish it still could be. Doctor's orders. Sometimes a cigar is just a cigar. And sometimes a bronze figurine of the goddess Isis suckling her infant son Horus, who grew to revenge the murder of his father, is… well, just another one of my treasures. Purchased, I may add, at a most reasonable price and worth more now than when I bought it.

VOICE: What can any mere dabbler ever know of the real passion for discovery? I was born to dig. I am an archaeologist by nature.

FREUD: *(really uneasy, looking around)* Where are you?

VOICE: Over here… Down here!

At last Freud sees: a head, severed from its body, a scientific specimen preserved in a jar—the head of another agèd, bearded man, the head of FLINDERS PETRIE.

The late Flinders Petrie

FREUD: Who are you?

PETRIE: Having overheard the utter nonsense you've been spouting I'd

217

venture to say with some confidence that I am The Voice of Reason.

FREUD: All my life I have been a champion, may I say a conquistador, for the Triumph of Reason.

PETRIE: *(sceptical)* Is that so? It should be me to ask: Who are *you*?

FREUD: *(with some pride)* There are those who call me: 'The Father of Psychoanalysis'.

PETRIE: In Egypt the fellahin call me 'The Father of Pots': Abu Bagousheh... I know which appellation I prefer.

FREUD: Did I not hear you say you were an archaeologist?

PETRIE: Indeed. And while we're on the subject of paternity, there are those who call *me* 'The Father of Archaeology.'

FREUD: Then it would seem we are both patriarchs.

PETRIE: You may have heard of me... My name is Flinders Petrie.

FREUD: *(pleasantly surprised)* Professor Petrie! And my reputation may also have preceded me. I am Sigmund Freud. I'm pleased to say I have read many of your books.

PETRIE: *(not so pleasantly surprised)* Doctor Freud? I'm equally pleased to say I've kept well away from yours.

FREUD: In fact, I have actually read more Archaeology than Psychology.

PETRIE: My profession requires engineers, not bookworms. How good are you at digging trenches?

FREUD: It is true that I have no interest in the actual routines of your profession.

PETRIE: Why am I not surprised? I dare say many folk think it's a very pleasant and easy sort of life in a tent. But how few are naturally suited to the never-ending toil, the spartan self-discipline of camp life? Not a soul within ten miles; nothing but rats, mice, fleas, sandstorms, brackish water, unpalatable supplies, disease-ridden marshes and desolation. No comfortable couch, no plush upholstered armchair on a dig. How would you consider leaving your study to cope with such conditions, Herr Doktor?

FREUD: I have never had to face the prospect, Mister Professor.

PETRIE: *(with fond remembrance)* And yet… I've much preferred the hard life I chose to the jangle of the modern world, the merciless rush, the rage for speed, the raucous twaddle of the gramophone, the turmoil of strife for money in staid, school-boarded England.

FREUD: I have found safety in your country. As an immigrant to England I have met with the friendliest reception. I live as a welcome guest. I can breathe a sigh of relief. A weight has been taken off me. I am once again able to speak, to write and—I almost said—to think, as I wish.

PETRIE: When the digging season came around I was only too happy to escape.

FREUD: I wonder… could you ever know the meaning of the word 'escape'?

PETRIE: Back to the silence of the desert. All around me that Great Peace. And all before me the prospect of unearthing long-lost remains of the forgotten past which no-one else has seen for so many thousands of years.

FREUD: Then I would venture to say, you and I have much in common.

PETRIE: I find that hard to imagine.

FREUD: I like to compare my work with the technique of excavating a buried city.

PETRIE: *(scornful)* Do you really, my dear sir? How so?

FREUD: I must follow the example set by a pioneering discoverer… such as yourself…

PETRIE: *(rather flattered)* Thank you.

FREUD: To bring to the light of day, after long entombment, relics of antiquity which, though they may perhaps be mutilated, are nonetheless priceless.

PETRIE: That has, indeed, been my life's work.

FREUD: Don't you see that I too must clear away the ruins to uncover what has long been hidden? The difference is that my excavation site is the human mind.

PETRIE: *(outraged)* Archaeology is a vocation, not a metaphor. In my profession one has to rub one's fingers in the mud. I have to work with dirty hands as well as with a clear head.

Looking intently at the head in the jar. After a pause, with delicacy:

FREUD: Speaking of which…

PETRIE: What?

FREUD: I couldn't help but wonder…

PETRIE: Oh, my head! I gave precise instructions for it to be surgically removed from my body, to be preserved in this jar and, in the fullness of time, to be donated to the Royal College of Surgeons.

FREUD: Forgive me if I enquire… for what purpose?

PETRIE: For eugenic study by future scientists as a perfect specimen of a typical English skull, of course. An analysis of my inherent nature may serve to prove that in England the foremost source of men of exceptional ability derives from the lineage of sturdy and virtuous puritan stock which has, throughout the ages, practised self-denial and hard work.

FREUD: Fascinating.

PETRIE: It is my express wish that this brain of mine might be subjected to histological analysis by those with the competent expertise to uncover the reason for the remarkable capacity I have always displayed for retaining the most minute facts… Facts, I emphasise, not fanciful theories. This brain, which has served me so well, will never be allowed to be subjected to the pokes and prods of a charlatan head-shrinker such as yourself. No, sir, there is nothing which could possibly unite us.

FREUD: Your resistance is most revealing.

PETRIE: I'll thank you to leave my mind alone and I shall leave you to gloat over the gleanings of your life-long obsession.

FREUD: Not an obsession. And certainly not life-long. Indeed, I did not begin this collection until I had reached my fifth decade… that was over forty years ago, back in 1896. *(wistful)* How strange to reflect I was only able to buy my very first piece *after* my father Jacob died…

PETRIE: *(equally moved)* How strange to recall I was only able to publish my work on the historical evidence for the sojourn of the Children of Israel in the land of Egypt *after* my father William died…

They are almost talking over each other… digging deep.

FREUD: Could it be that the very act of collecting filled a void for me? That it provided a consolation, an invigoration and yes, perhaps even a renewal during this time of grieving?

PETRIE: Could it be that the old man's death...

FREUD: ...the most significant event, the most poignant loss of any man's life...

PETRIE: ...granted me the freedom to contradict in public the Biblical account of the Book of Exodus? The fruits of my research would surely have seemed a sacrilege to a man of his sincere and unshakeable belief.

FREUD: Could it be that the old man's death granted *me* the liberation to hold in my hand objects his religion proscribed as...

TOGETHER: 'Idols of wood and stone'.

FREUD: My dear father was a devout Jew...

PETRIE: My father—no less dear to me than yours was to you—was a member of the Brethren, fundamentally accepting every chapter and verse of the Scriptures as the revealed word of Almighty God.

FREUD: The second commandment of Moses prohibits the worship of graven images...

PETRIE: So this is why you began collecting: to defy the Law of your Father?

FREUD: So... you have become the psychoanalyst now?

PETRIE: *(blustering)* I was merely...

FREUD: *(interrupting)* Thinking of your own life? So this is why you began digging: to challenge the Faith of your Father?

PETRIE: Not at all. I owe everything I am to him.

FREUD: All I can say is that these Egyptian antiquities of mine seem to speak of distant times and far-off places.

PETRIE: Then why say more?

FREUD: They exercise a powerful effect on me... they seem to awaken strange secret yearnings... for the East... for my paternal heritage... *(stopping himself)* Was it the stories in your father's Bible that made you decide your future lay in Egypt?

PETRIE: Enough! Perhaps it's best for both of us if we speak no more of our fathers.

FREUD:	Which art in heaven? Or still, perhaps, living within us?
PETRIE:	That's quite sufficient!
FREUD:	The more you resist the more I sense you are begging me to dig deeper.
PETRIE:	I shall keep my psychology to myself, thank you very much. My work has meant I've had no occasion for morbid dwelling on the inner life. *(attempting to leave, to disappear)* My time with you is at an end.
FREUD:	*(stopping him)* A moment please… I must take the opportunity for a discussion with the most esteemed of all Egyptologists.
PETRIE:	Very well… Provided it's nothing personal.
FREUD:	I cannot promise that. Is there any subject which does not come out of, and return us to, the deepest regions of our own psyche?
PETRIE:	I have no notion of what you're talking about.
FREUD:	I am most interested in your excavation at Tell el Amarna.
PETRIE:	*(relieved)* Now we are on firmer ground: Akhetaten.
FREUD:	City of the heretical pharaoh.
PETRIE:	Palace of the revolutionary pharaoh: Akhenaten.
FREUD:	Akhenaten. It is he who fascinates me.
PETRIE:	Everything you've read about him ultimately derives from *my* work… my excavations in the capital he built more than thirteen hundred years before Christ which had lain buried and deserted for over three thousand years.
FREUD:	If I recall… you describe Akhenaten as the most original thinker who ever lived in Egypt.
PETRIE:	Far more than that: One of the greatest idealists the world has ever known. *(as if transported)* The purity of his thought… the modernity of his philosophy… the boldness of his endeavour… the courage of his convictions…
FREUD:	You speak as if you knew him personally.
PETRIE:	I have looked into his face… I feel that I have searched his very soul.
FREUD:	His face? Ah, the death-mask. I have, of course, seen pictures…

PETRIE: And I have held it in my hands. Entirely unlike any other stylised depiction of the Kings of the Two Lands. This is the face of a real human being... a living man who thought and loved... revealing a delicacy of feeling; a kindness of manner; an evident sense of humour; a fond enjoyment of everyday pleasures; a devotion to his four little daughters and a touching adoration of his beautiful wife, Nefertiti...

Akhenaten's Death Mask

(stopping as if embarrassed) Doubtless you think my enthusiasm somewhat imaginative.

FREUD: On the contrary, I always find the exercise of the imagination most illuminating.

PETRIE: You call this 'imagination'? Imagination may be a fine servant, but it is the worst of all masters. I assure you, I have witnessed Akhenaten's wonderful character written in his face as clear as if I had seen him in the flesh. The Prince of Aten, son of the sun.

FREUD: The founder of monotheism...

PETRIE: Far, far much more than that. He did not worship some deity who made the sun... nor even the sun itself. He allowed no primitive human or animal form to depict the Aten. This was a purely abstract doctrine.

FREUD: No magic... No sorcery... No amulets... No idols... No animal-headed gods... No superstition... No illusion... No wars, no brutal imperial expansion in this king's reign.

PETRIE: Somehow—and who can say how?—Akhenaten arrived at the knowledge which the most forward-thinkers of our own day have only now come to understand: The profound truth that it is the *rays* of the sun which are the source of all life, power and force in the universe. If a new religion were invented to satisfy our modern scientific conceptions we could not find a flaw in the correctness of his view of the energy of the solar system. If only today's rulers could appreciate such ethical purity as Akhenaten's own people never could. *(a sigh)* Alas. Your attraction to this great soul is well founded.

FREUD: *(not without some embarrassment)* I am afraid my especial interest is not entirely dispassionate. It relates to an incident from my own life, the memory of which continues to cause some occasional anxiety. It was in 1912… I was attending the annual Psychoanalytic Congress in Munich. Karl Abraham, one of my disciples…

PETRIE: 'Disciples'! Who do you think you are: Jesus?

FREUD: … was preparing a paper to demonstrate that our psychoanalytic method can be applied to figures from history… not just to the troubled folk of these times who place their problems in our hands.

PETRIE: More fool they. Self-obsessed malingerers with more money than sense.

FREUD: The character he had chosen for this study was none other than Akhenaten.

PETRIE: Is nothing… no-one… sacred?

FREUD: Our discussion naturally turned to the change of his identity. In adopting the cult of the Aten…

PETRIE: *(with disdain)* You call it a 'cult?' No such grand theology had ever before appeared in the world.

FREUD: …In prohibiting the worship of all previous polytheistic divinities, the young king rejected not only the gods of his childhood, but even his own former name, the name he had been given at birth…

PETRIE: Teaching grandmother to suck eggs, are we now?

FREUD: For he had been dedicated to the god *Amen*, presiding deity of Thebes—whose temples he would turn his back upon to found his own city.

PETRIE: Akhetaten: 'Horizon of the Aten'—which, let me remind you, was lost to sight and memory until my excavations brought it to the light of day.

FREUD: Thus *Amen*hotep...

PETRIE: 'Amen is satisfied'

FREUD: ...transformed himself into Akhen*aten*...

PETRIE: 'Glory of the Aten.'

FREUD: ... And gave orders to strike out his former name from every one of the monuments previously raised to him. This iconoclasm, perforce, also required him to have the name of his own father: *Amen*hotep the Third...

PETRIE: The Magnificent, ninth ruler of the Eighteenth dynasty...

FREUD: ... erased from all cartouches on the stelae of *his* reign. Akhenaten had literally to wipe away the Name of the Father.

PETRIE: You are obsessed with fathers.

FREUD: Is not every son?

PETRIE: I thought we had agreed—no more mention of fathers.

FREUD: Not, I'm afraid, so easy.

PETRIE: My patience has its limits.

FREUD: Please, indulge me a moment further. *(an attempt at humour?)* Abraham—I refer to the German analyst, not the Biblical patriarch—not unreasonably postulated that Akhenaten's heresy...

PETRIE: Reformation...

FREUD: ... must have been the result of a neurosis.

PETRIE: Nonsense!

FREUD: Underlying his apparently humanistic compulsion to create a new monotheistic religion lay a sinister desire...

PETRIE: Really, I can take no more!

FREUD: The unconscious desire... to murder his father!

PETRIE: No evidence whatsoever!

FREUD: With us on that day was another of my disciples...

PETRIE: How many more of them? I'd be amazed if you could muster a full dozen.

225

FREUD: Carl Jung had been the most favoured of my followers, almost a surrogate son to me. He was the one I had intended, in the event of some unforeseen occurrence to myself, to take my place at the head of our growing movement. As Abraham expounded his hypothesis…

PETRIE: Fairy tale…

FREUD: …Jung became increasingly agitated. He persisted in his disingenuous protestation that Akhenaten was no neurotic…

PETRIE: Hear, hear.

FREUD: But rather a profoundly spiritual person whose religious reforms should not be reduced to a father-complex.

PETRIE: My view entirely.

FREUD: Jung insisted that the zeal for destruction was directed towards the god Amen, not the man Amenhotep.

PETRIE: Sounds like the one person of some sense amidst a crowd of maniacs.

FREUD: As the argument continued to rage with increasing bitterness I do not clearly remember what came over me. Apparently, I fell off my chair in a dead faint. It was Jung who picked me up and carried me to lay down upon a sofa. Despite this apparent concern for my welfare, as I looked into his eyes at that moment, I saw in them an unconscious desire to erase me as Akhenaten had erased his own father.

PETRIE: Which one of your disciples was he? Judas?

FREUD: Shortly thereafter Jung, the one I had chosen to be my successor, broke off all contact with me and set up his own practice in opposition to my own.

PETRIE: *(finally losing patience with such a memory)* What, may I ask, is the point of this anecdote and its relevance to my archaeological discoveries?

FREUD: What, I may answer, more cogent illustration could there be of the pertinence of my psychoanalytic discoveries?

PETRIE: Of one thing I can be certain in this uncertain world: Your fantastic presumptions will be swept away on the ocean of Time.

FREUD: Exactly like Akhenaten? Whose successors all too swiftly abandoned his principles?

PETRIE: His city was deserted and destroyed with the greatest zeal…
            Not one stone was left in place.

FREUD: Vindictive priests led a panic-stricken people back to the
            secure sanctuary of their old gods.

PETRIE: The plundering, conquering, pompous cruelty and self-
            glorification of pharaonic rule was restored. The names of
            Akhenaten and his queen were erased…

FREUD: As he had erased the name of his father.

PETRIE: The worship of the Aten was prohibited…

Israel in Egypt from Phillippson's Bible

FREUD: As Akhenaten had prohibited the worship of Amen, of Ra, of Isis and Osiris…

PETRIE: The Egyptians rushed on into an age of warfare and decadence. Does that chime with our present age? You see, I too have my theories. My contention is that civilisation turns in cycles. And I fully suspect we are entering a cycle of despair.

FREUD: Of discontent.

PETRIE: Akhenaten's thoughts died with him… As yours will with you.

FREUD: Perhaps not… *(a revelation)* What if one of *his* persecuted disciples fled and took his advanced idea of one universal God, creator and sustainer, to a despised tribe enslaved in the Land of Goshen?

PETRIE: *(surprised)* The Jews?

FREUD: What if Moses, the man who introduced monotheistic religion to the Hebrews, was an *Egyptian*?

PETRIE: Are you seeking to deny your own heritage? To transform the foundation of your people's religion? *(after a thought)* Oh, I'm beginning to get the hang of this game of yours: this is another act of revenge against your father.

FREUD: The man who has the courage to rebel against his father, the man who has, in the end, victoriously overcome him… that is the very definition of a hero.

PETRIE: From a historical perspective: gibberish!

FREUD: But from a psychological perspective: only too probable.

PETRIE: What right have you to advance these speculations? You've never even set foot in the Land of the Pharoahs.

FREUD: *(with regret)* Indeed… I shall be ferried over the River Styx before ever crossing the River Nile.

PETRIE: *(with equal regret)* And I shall never set eyes upon my beloved Egypt again. *(after a pause)* This I will grant you: There is so much of which we must remain in ignorance. All work is but an uncompleted intention. All I leave as my future legacy are fragments.

FREUD: Fragments… Stepping-stones on the royal road to the unconscious…

PETRIE: That stone the others rejected as worthless…

FREUD: Has become…

PETRIE: As the psalmist said…

FREUD: The cornerstone upon which the whole building stands.

PETRIE: Debris of everyday life…

FREUD: Remnants awaiting to be uncovered…

PETRIE: Tiny splinters buried in some humble abode…

FREUD: Childhood fantasies half-remembered…

PETRIE: More momentous than those 'wonderful things' discovered in the tomb of Tutankhamen.

FREUD: Dreams to be interpreted…

PETRIE: Hieroglyphs to be deciphered……

FREUD: Jokes to be unravelled…

PETRIE: Broken potsherds to be dated…

FREUD: Slips of the tongue to be decoded…

PETRIE: Inscriptions hitherto ignored to be translated…

FREUD: Before *me* who would have thought such unconsidered trifles worthy of analysis?

PETRIE: Before *me* who would have given any value to discarded objects not worth sixpence in the markets of the dealers in antiquities?

FREUD: Opening the sealed door…

PETRIE: Letting fresh air into the silence of the sepulchre…

FREUD: Memories long repressed…

PETRIE: Digging through the silt, the clay, the soil…

FREUD: Layer upon layer…

PETRIE: Dirtying our hands…

FREUD: Crumbling in our grasp…

PETRIE: As we expose them to the light of day…

FREUD: As we retrieve them from the Id to the Ego…

PETRIE: Preserving…

FREUD:	Conserving…
PETRIE:	Slipping through our fingers…
FREUD:	Like the sands of Egypt…
PETRIE:	Before they are lost forever.
FREUD:	Then you must agree, we do have much in common.
PETRIE:	Of that you will never persuade me. I am but a salvage man…
FREUD:	What else am I?
PETRIE:	But at least I can say I did my duty.
FREUD:	Are we not both excavators?
PETRIE:	If so, we have been digging in different mounds.
FREUD:	'Living in Truth'.
PETRIE:	*Ankh em maat.*
FREUD:	The inscription on Akhenaten's cartouche.
PETRIE:	A motto I have taken as my own.
FREUD:	An epigraph I hope the future will allow me.

Akhenaten and his family worship the Aten

PETRIE: Will those who follow after strike out our names from our monuments?

FREUD: As Akhenaten erased the name of his father?

PETRIE: My head is tired.

FREUD: This is all that I can offer.

TOGETHER: Living in Truth. Dying in Illusion.

THE END

ABOUT THE AUTHOR

Michael Eaton is an award-winning dramatist for cinema, television, radio and the theatre who has written TV docu-dramas such as *Why Lockerbie*, the BAFTA nominated *Shoot to Kill* and *Shipman* for ITV and original dramas including *Signs and Wonders* and *Flowers Of The Forest* for the BBC. His script for the HBO feature film *Fellow Traveller* won Best Screenplay at the British Film Awards in 1989. He has written four plays for Nottingham Playhouse of which the last was *Charlie Peace – His Amazing Life and Astounding Legend*, also the subject of his 2017 publication. He has adapted several works of Charles Dickens for BBC Radio 4 including *The Pickwick Papers* starring Timothy Spall; *George Silverman's Explanation* with Paul Scofield; *The Bride's Chamber* and *The Special Correspondent for Posterity* which was commissioned for the Dickens bicentenary of 2012 for which he also co-wrote and narrated an Arena documentary: *Dickens and Film*. His theatrical adaptation of *Great Expectations* premiered at the West Yorkshire Playhouse in 2016. Other original radio plays include *Washington 9/11; The Conflict Is Over* (about the Northern Ireland peace process); *Out of the Blue; By A Young Officer – Churchill on the North-West Frontier* and, with the composer Neil Brand, *The Cave of Harmony* and *Waves Breaking On A Shore*. His adaptation of Agatha Christie's *Murder On The Orient Express* for Audible was the winner of the first Cameo Book-to-Audio award 2018. He studied Social Anthropology at King's College, Cambridge and, thirty-five years later, made *The Masks of Mer*, a documentary film about the anthropologist Alfred Haddon which was also the subject of his 2015 BBC Radio 3 drama *Head Hunters*. The text of this was published by Shoestring Press which also published his translation of Ernest Renan's French play *The Priest of Nemi*. He was awarded the M.B.E. for Services to Film in the 1999 New Year's honours list and was Visiting Professor in the School of Creative Writing at Nottingham Trent University for which institution he wrote a play, *All Schools Should Be Art Schools*, to commemorate the 170th anniversary of the foundation of the Nottingham School of Art. He is to receive a Doctorate of Letters from NTU in 2020.